TALES OF THE FLORIDA SUNCOAST

TALES OF THE
Florida Suncoast

By JACK BEATER

(Member: Authors League of America)

Designed by

Great Outdoors Association

PRESIDENT

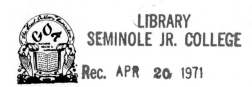
Produced by

GREAT OUTDOORS PUBLISHING COMPANY

St. Petersburg, Fla.

MEET THE *Author*

JACK BEATER

JACK BEATER, the author of many books and short stories covering numerous facets of the Florida scene, was born in Philadelphia, Pennsylvania, just before the turn of the century. After living in Missouri, California, New Jersey, Cuba, and seven years in Mexico City, he graduated from Penn State University in time to join the Army as an instructor in the First World War. In 1920 he came to South Florida for a two weeks visit—and remained.

He was engaged in both business and writing for a number of years, then decided to give up the business of commerce for the business of writing. Since then he has seen the publication of many books, and hundreds of articles. In 1950 he was elected to membership in The Authors League of America, a society of professional writers. He is married, lives on Mc-Gregor Boulevard in Fort Myers, Florida, and has no children.

Contents

Foreword

OR MORE than forty-five years I have been traveling up and down Florida's Suncoast with notebook and pencil in hand, and set down many stories of interest, and off-beat facts. Now, with this book, a number of these assorted tales have been set into type. Many of the people mentioned herein I have known at first hand; other stories were told to me by friends, relatives or officers of the law. A few items were clipped from the regional press, but in all cases the stories have a basis of fact. Names and places have been changed in certain cases, and for good and sufficient reasons, but any of the names of my invention which may happen to be the same as any real person, living or dead, are purely coincidental.

In the case of "The Nurse From Mendigo Key" I have taken the liberty of combining two separate romances into one story, and in "Bradenton's Bad Boy" I have purposely left out quite a few of the sordid details. In "A Whale Of A Times At Naples" I personally counted and paced off the length of the unfortunate denizens of the deep, and the "Wild Life" story is quite true to fact. Other stories from my many notebooks will be found in the other books of this series — TALES OF SOUTH FLORIDA PIONEERS, and PIRATES AND BURIED TREASURE ON FLORIDA ISLANDS. I trust you will find something of merit in the following pages.

JACK BEATER

The Fall and Rise of Bonnie Becker

Time: 1930 *to* 1950   *Place: Tampa Bay Area*

ONNIE BECKER WAS BORN in 1918 and she was an only child. It was a good thing, because her father, Henry Becker, was a handy man around a cigar box factory, and drank up so much of his wages that his wife and child were always in want. They lived in a three room house that was little more than a shack, in the 22nd Street neighborhood of Tampa, down near the bay.

Bonnie was a robust child of six when she started school, and several of the neighbors remarked that the chubby, red haired girl, with the deep blue eyes, bore a striking resemblance to a collector for a loan company who used to call at the Becker house while Henry Becker was at work. This went on until Bonnie was eight, and then Henry Becker was killed by a hit and run driver, and the red haired loan company collector moved in with Mrs. Becker and little Bonnie without benefit of clergy.

At twelve Bonnie was the leader of the neighborhood children. When she was around the street rang with the cries and laughter of the boys and girls, and if there was any mischief afoot it was a safe bet that Bonnie was in the middle of it. There were people who whispered that she was a wayward girl, and would come to no good, but there were others who liked the teen-aged girl with the parted lips and laughing eyes. Perhaps it was due to the fact that Bonnie was always soft spoken and polite to adults.

A change came over Bonnie in her fourteenth year. Inner pressures began to stir and form a pattern for the coming years. Little by little over a period of months, she began to ignore the girls she had played with, and took up with some of the older boys. Some of the neighbors who happened to look out of a window at just the right moment shook their heads in disapproval. No good could come of a girl acting that way—letting a boy take liberties with her person. Near neighbors who knew the family secrets whispered among themselves.

"Like mother, like daughter, I always say," Mrs. Cathy Reeves remarked to Mrs. Tillie Koppenkeffer.

"You said it!" Tillie came back. "That Bonnie will grow up to be a chippie, or I miss my guess."

When she was fifteen Bonnie ran away from home. One of the neighborhood boys was missing, too. He was Curtis Evans, aged eighteen. He had been working at a fish house on Saturdays and Sundays, and it was known that he had saved up all of twenty dollars. He had bragged that he had enough money to go away on a trip, and had a girl who was willing and waiting.

Bonnie and Curt came home at the end of five days. They had been married, and had the certificate to prove it. They might not have come back home, but Bonnie was suffering. She couldn't sit still a minute; she had to keep scratching all the time. It was not only annoying, but embarassing, too. Bonnie's mother investigated and sent the girl to a doctor. The girl's abdoman seemed to be broken out in a firey rash.

The doctor made an examination, asked a few questions, then stated his findings. It wasn't a rash at all. It was just a bad case of redbugs—those tiny insects that burrow under the skin and start housekeeping. He gave Bonnie some salve and said the itching would stop in about ten days— after the bugs were dead.

For the next few weeks Bonnie met smiles wherever she went. The details of the short honeymoon, and the story behind the redbug infestation had spread until the whole neighborhood knew.

It seemed that Curt and Bonnie had applied for a marriage license in Tampa, but the clerk had turned them down because they were under age and lacked the parents' consent.

When they got out on the street Curt and Bonnie talked it over. Why not? The clerk had shown them a way to circumvent the law. Within an hour the boy and girl had hitched a ride on a fish truck, and were in the next county. On the edge of the county seat there was a wooded stream, and Curt and Bonnie paused to gather a double armful of Spanish moss which had fallen from the live oaks along the bank. In a little while they walked into town and asked directions to the Courthouse.

The County Judge proved to be a kind and understanding man. He gave one look at Bonnie, and then turned to Curt. "Guess I'll have to marry you," he said, "and it's not any too soon. The law allows me to use my discretion in cases of this kind, so let's get it over with."

In truth Bonnie was not pregnant, but she said she was, and all the outward evidence seemed to support her claim. How was the soft hearted judge to know that there was nothing under her clothing but a large wad of Spanish moss resting next to her skin? That, and a thousand tiny redbugs eager to find a new home. When the itching became unbearable, and Curt's money was about gone, Bonnie could think only of getting home to her mother.

The marriage of Bonnie and Curt lasted a bare fourteen months. The blame was Bonnie's of course, for she was not only hearstrong but unreasonable. She had been seen in cars with other boys, and the neighbors knew that she had entertained several young men in the house while her mother and Curt were at work. When Curt found out how things were going he moved out and got a divorce a year or two later.

For the next ten years Bonnie was a waitress in a Greek restaurant, a ticket taker at a drive-in-movie, and then a car hop at a second-rate juke joint out beyond the 22nd Street Causeway, going south.

She liked this last job best of all, and did well in gathering tips. Most of the customers were truck drivers, salesmen, or young men out on the make. When she could she left the teen-agers and love-sick couples to the other girls. She soon learned to cater to the older men. It wasn't only because they tipped better, but because they showed a girl more respect. They weren't as silly and demanding, and they expected to have to pay for any favors.

Bonnie worked the night shift at the drive-in — from 6 p.m. to 2 a.m. Sometimes, if a man looked like a good sport and said the right things, she'd let him take her for a ride after closing time. She could sleep all day, so she didn't mind being kept out 'til almost daylight. When her mother scolded about the hours she kept it did little good. Bonnie reminded her mother of her age—25—and threatened to move out.

Bonnie drifted into her new profession with her eyes open, but she tried not to be cheap or common about it. She was particular about the men she dated, and there were a good many nights when she went straight home to please her mother. Her tips came to something like fifteen or twenty dollars a week, and she made another twenty or so on the side. She gave her mother ten dollars a week towards running the house, spent about ten on herself, and used the rest to pay off the doctor and hospital for her mother's last operation.

Trouble came to Bonnie on a warm night in the summer of 1943. It was a Monday, the slowest night of the week, and when a car drove in with an army officer at the wheel, it was Bonnie who got there first. She liked to wait on officers for they had more money and tipped better than the soldiers from the air base.

After she had placed the officer's order on the car door, Bonnie went into her act. She had a good figure, and she had learned how best to bring it to a man's attention. She stepped back from the car, put her hands against her trim waist, and slowly turned around to show her profile. She had practiced before a mirror and she knew how to make the most of her hundred and thirty-five pounds. She was no beauty, she knew, but her red hair, laughing eyes and creamy skin without a blemish, made most men turn for a second look.

The man in the car, Captain Mark Haskell, motioned to Bonnie. "Look, honey!" he said when she came close, "I've got nothing special to do—and all night to do it in. You know a girl I could get for a ride to the beach and a swim?"

"We don't close for two hours," Bonnie answered, "but things are slow and the boss might let me off. Want me to ask him?"

"We got a deal cooking," the Captain said. "Go ask him—I'll wait."

Bonnie settled up her tickets with the cashier, picked up her purse from the girls' locker room, and went outside. The Captain had turned the car around, and was headed in the direction of the nearest public beach. As soon as she was in the car she knew the officer had been drinking, but he wasn't drunk. She felt a liquor flask on the seat, and when he wasn't looking she lowered it to the floor and kicked it under the seat.

The car passed the last of the lights of a village, then settled down to a fast pace through the night. As she was sure he would, he took a hand from the wheel, caught her shoulder, and drew her close. When his head twisted she felt his whiskey breath on her cheek. There was a brief struggle. The car was doing 70 and she wanted him to keep his mind on the driving. As she pulled away her hand felt something cold jammed into the space between the back of the seat and the cushion. It was the Captain's service automatic. For the first time in her life Bonnie felt a premonition of trouble, but it was too late to turn back.

When they reached the beach the Captain stopped a couple hundred yards from the last cottage, and put out the lights. The south end of the beach was still about as nature made it. Bathers and picknickers used it by day, and sometimes a man and a maid went there at night. Captain Haskell got out of the car and went around to Bonnie's side.

"End of the line," he said. "Come on, you—get out!"

*   *   *   *

When Mrs. Paul Hess left her cottage for an early stroll along the beach on Tuesday morning she was totally unprepared for the horrible sight she was soon to meet. She had gone but a hundred yards or so beyond the last cottage when she thought she heard, above the sound of the surf, a muted cry of "Help!"

Some fifty yards away, up near the sea oats growing along the fringe of the beach, Mrs. Hess saw a sign of movement. At first glance it looked like a man playing in the coarse sand—a man in red swim trunks. As she gazed she saw that it was a human body, and saw an arm raise up in a feeble gesture. Again she heard the weak cry of "Help!"

Mrs. Hess dropped some shells she had collected on the beach, and started towards the strange figure. She wondered what a man was doing on the beach so early, and with no car nearby. She thought he might be sick—have swimmers' cramps. If he was really sick she'd have to go back for help.

As Mrs. Hess drew near the man tried to hunch up on his knees, but he couldn't make it. He made a whimper like a wounded animal, then fell over with his face to the sky. Mrs. Hess stopped in her tracks and gasped. The man wasn't wearing red trunks—he was naked. The red coloring about his stomach and hips was blood mixed with beach sand. She heard the man's breath gurgle through the froth on his lips. He was almost dead! Horror stricken, the woman turned and ran screaming down the beach.

*   *   *   *

The County Coroner and the deputy sheriff arrived together and began their investigation. The man had been shot in the abdomen, and had bled to death on the sand. The first find was a woman's brassiere beside the tire tracks where a car had been parked, and the second thing was a man's wallet with cards and identification, but no money. It had been thrown into a clump of sea oats. The tire tracks showed that the car had been driven away at high speed.

Inside of six hours the police were looking for Bonnie Becker. Several girls at the drive-in had volunteered the information that Bonnie had driven off with an army officer of the dead man's description, and she had not returned home. Then Captain Haskell's car was found up in the middle of the state where it had run out of gas. Two days later Bonnie walked into a Highway Patrol Station and gave herself up.

"The man got drunk and real mean," Bonnie told the officers. "He was going to kill me and I had to shoot him with his own gun. I didn't want to do it, but he was choking me — awful. Look, you can still see the marks on my throat!"

When Bonnie was brought into the County Jail she was still wearing the same green dress she'd worn the night of the murder. The next day her mother came down from Tampa and brought her another dress and some underclothes, then went back home to await the trial.

"If I ever get out of this mess," Bonnie told her mother. "I'm going to try and write a story about how I got into a spot where I had to kill a man. It won't help me none, but it might teach other girls not to go with strange men."

*   *   *   *

Elmer Knull walked towards Main Street, and as he walked little animal-like sounds came from his throat. He had a habit of talking to himself. That was why some of the town people thought Elmer was sort of crazy, and went out of their way to avoid him. It wasn't because he was dangerous, or anymg like that. The opposite was true. Some people thought he was "touched" because of his almost perpetual grin, but there'd never been any thought of locking him up.

Elmer was a steady, plodding worker, and he had a way with animals. He was thirty-five, single, and since the age of fifteen he'd been working for Jube Maxwell, the diaryman. According to Jube, Elmer had a way of making mewing sounds in his throat that caused cows to let down more milk, and soothed the meanest of the herd bulls. All animals—dogs, cats, mules, even chickens, seemed to understand the man's mutterings.

Jube Maxwell and his wife, Elsa, as well as a few other people, knew Elmer Knull for what he really was; a tender hearted soul with simple thoughts and simple habits. He was a simple man, but not simple minded, was the way one person put it.

Elmer's thoughts, whatever they were, were interrupted as he passed along the side of the County Jail. A girl inside the bars of a second floor window called down to him.

"Hey, you, mister!" he heard her yell, "Give me a couple cigarettes, will yuh?"

"I don't smoke," said Elmer looking up at the bars, "but I get you some — you just wait."

"Poor girl . . . locked up in jailhouse . . . want cigarettes . . . I got money . . . I can buy . . . " Such were Elmer's thoughts as he hurried to Main Street and entered a corner cafe. "Cigarettes — two packs," he said to the cashier.

"What brand?" the girl wanted to know.

"No difference," Pete grinned. He held out a crumpled dollar bill. "Two packs . . . any kind."

Deputy Sheriff Locke, the jailer, was taking it easy when Elmer came up the jail steps. "Hello, Elmer," he called out, "you looking for room and board?"

Elmer grinned and held out the packs of cigarettes. "For the girl up there . . . " He threw his eyes up the iron stairs to the second floor. "She wants smokes . . . so I bring some."

"Well, that's what I call being real neighborly," said the jailer. He was Jube Maxwell's brother-in-law, and knew all about Elmer. "Suppose you take them up yourself," he suggested. "With my bad knee, goin' up and down those steps is gettin' to be murder."

The next day Elmer was back at the jail, and this time he had a carton of cigarettes and a paper bag. "What you got in the sack?" the jailer wanted to know.

"Candy!" Elmer grinned. "Chocolate bars—caramels —chewing gum. You don't mind, Mr. Locke?"

"If you want to squander your money on a slut, it's your business," said the Deputy. "Go on, take 'em up if you want to."

From then on Elmer was a frequent visitor at the jail while Bonnie Becker was awaiting trial. Each time he brought something under his arms; more cigarettes and candy, some confession magazines, cheap perfume, toilet soap, and things from the bakery.

"It was the darndest thing you ever saw," Deputy Locke told Sheriff Reeves one Saturday night. "I was sittin' at the desk this afternoon when I heard some heavin' and puffin' out on the jail steps. Up comes Elmer Knull dragging an overstuffed platform rocker. I said, 'What the hell's goin' on . . . ? Then Elmer explained."

" 'I brought it for Bonnie,' he tells me. I already suspected that, so I asked, 'Why?' "

"It's for Bonnie to sit in," Elmer explained to the Deputy. "She's heavy-like, and sittin' on the edge of the iron bed hurts the back of her legs."

Bonnie Becker went to trial in mid-November, and she looked very nice in the new dress and shoes Elmer Knull had paid for. The peoples' case was brief and to the point. The prosecutor called her act, "the brutal murder of a man for the few paltry dollars in his purse."

Bonnie's lawyer had been appointed by the court. He was Harold Holtz, a young fellow just out of law school. His first witnesses were two girls from Tampa who admitted to having had dates with the murdered man, Captain Haskell. Both testified as to having been mistreated by the man, and said they considered themselves lucky to have escaped without some form of lasting bodily harm.

"And now, gentlemen of the jury," Harold Holtz began his final plea, "try to picture yourself in the place of this young woman on that dreadful night. You are a woman alone on a deserted beach—in the dead of night—with a drunken man fired with evil intent. You are being chased —naked—by a madman, you fear for your very life. Suddenly you recall a revolver—in this case an automatic—on the seat of the car. Remember, gentlemen, it was his gun, not hers. Can you blame this young woman for trying to protect herself? She grabs the gun—she shoots as a last resort. She shoots, not with the thought to kill, but just to make good her own escape. Who are we to say that in her place we wouldn't have done the same?"

The woman, Holtz repeated, only did what she had every right to do. She had a God given right to defend herself from the sadistic intentions of a drunken and savage brute. If the gun was her only means, then she had a right to use it in self defense.

"The State's Attorney has made much of the fact that the defendant took time after the shooting, to remove nine paltry dollars from the man's bill fold," said Harold Holtz in conclusion. "About the taking of the money I have only one thing to say. According to established law a laborer is worthy of his hire. Bonnie Becker, in ways of her own, had earned a part of that money. She had established a claim against it—part of it was hers by right. She had no means of making change or deciding what part was rightfully hers in her hysterical condition, so she took it all. Wrong, you say? Yes, she did do wrong, but it was an error of judgment, not of intent. Any one of you, if faced by the same conditions, might have reacted in the same manner. As I see it this poor woman is guilty of only one thing—taking a few paltry dollars that were not hers—three or four dollars at the most. If you leave that out what have you left in this case? Nothing, I tell you, but a simple case of justifiable homicide."

The jury was out less than half an hour. There was a smattering of applause when the verdict was read. It was manslaughter with a recommendation of mercy. Both lawyers were quick on their feet and waived the right to appeal. The Judge called the prisoner to the bench.

"Eight years," he said. "Eight years to be served in the Women's Division of the State Prison."

A month or two after Bonnie Becker's conviction one of the fact detective magazines sent a writer to Florida to write a detailed story of the case, and it was later published in all the gory details, as the CASE OF THE MAN IN THE RED 'TRUNKS'.

There is little more to tell. Elmer Knull wrote to Bonnie almost every week while she was in prison, and he sent her gifts from time to time. Elmer Knull, dressed in the first matching suit he'd ever owned, was waiting at the prison gate when Bonnie was released for good behavior at the end of six years. He was driving Jube Maxwell's new station wagon, and as soon as they reached the town of Starke, Florida, they were married. They spent a day visiting Bonnie's mother in Tampa, then Elmer returned to his job at the dairy farm.

Bonnie received quite a surprise when they reached the Maxwell farm. Elmer drove up to a new cottage fronting on the main highway, and carried Bonnie over the threshhold exactly like Mrs. Jube Maxwell had told him to do. The house had five rooms, all furnished, and was to be paid for a little a month like rent. And with no interest. The electric range, water heater and deep freeze were wedding presents from the Maxwells.

In 1955 the same writer who had done the 'sin and suffer' story on the Becker-Haskell murder case for the crime story magazine, returned to town. He had been sent to do a possible 'follow-up' story on Bonnie Becker since her release from prison. He called on the Sheriff, and Jube Maxwell, and stopped to talk with Bonnie and Elmer. What he learned is best told in a note he sent back to the editor in New York.

" . . . the follow-up on the Becker-Haskell murder case is a dud. No story here. Bonnie Becker is married, has 2 kids, a boy and girl. Local Sheriff says Mrs. Elmer

Knull—her married name—has been in no trouble. Husband's employer says they are a model couple— best worker he ever had. Buying their own home, doing well. Bonnie says her husband is best ever—never angry, always kind and considerate. He says Bonnie is a good wife . . . good cook, good with kids, good with chickens. In other words this Bonnie has become a respectable housewife and mother—no story value at all. Leaving today for next assignment you sent me. Let's hope I find some real, gooey pay DIRT on the next job. This Bonnie turned out to be a complete flop. Sorry."

'Being of Sound Mind and Memory'

Time: 1957   *Place*: *Clearwater*

 MET DONALD BARTON for the first time when we were the guests of Rufe Reece, the playright, and his good wife, Katie, aboard their new and luxurious cabin cruiser, the KISS-ME-KATE. The junket was in the nature of a shake-down cruise, and we were headed for the Ten Thousand Island region and White Water Bay. When Don Barton told us the following story we were anchored in Lemon Bay, near the town of Englewood in southern Sarasota County. I had just idly mentioned that a close friend had died, and that his widow had asked my advice on some investments.

"Well, don't give her any!" Don Barton exclaimed bluntly. "Trying to help a widow—one who has money— is a sure way to make a lot of trouble for yourself. Me? I ought to know—let me tell you about the trouble I've been through. Women—especially old women—Bah!"

Don proceeded to tell the pain and anguish he had suffered from trying to be a good Samaritan, and later the same night I made notes on his discourse. This is the story Don told us in the cabin of the KISS-ME-KATE:

Anna Muller was born in Germany in 1874, and came to live with a sister in Chicago when she was thirteen. At

21

the age of twenty she went to work as housekeeper for a man named Milton T. Jarrett. Mrs. Jarrett was a semi-invalid, and the new housekeeper, Anna Muller, soon took over complete control of the premises, and replaced the cook and upstairs maid with ones of her own choosing.

The new upstairs maid was a German immigrant who couldn't speak a word of English. Her name was Berta Krell, and even though she remained with Anna Muller for the next sixty-two years, first as a servant, then as a companion, she never learned to speak much English, and never received more than her room, board, clothes and a little notion money from time to time.

About a year after Anna Muller became housekeeper, the ailing Mrs. Jarrett took a turn for the worse, and died suddenly under somewhat peculiar circumstances. Nothing came of the investigation, and Mr. Jarrett kept Anna on to run the home for himself and his son, Wilbert. Just what sort of attachment developed between Wilbert and the housekeeper — they were only a year apart in age — has always remained unclear, but the fact is that they lived in the same house until Wilbert's death some fifty-nine years later.

Two years after Mrs. Jarrett's death the friends of the Jarrett family were shocked to learn that Milton Jarrett had secretly married his housekeeper, Anna Muller. Milton Jarrett was fifty-nine at the time, his son was twenty-five, Anna was twenty-four, and the maid, Berta, was twenty-three. The four continued to live together in the big house in North Chicago, and gossip flew thick and fast.

The main reason for the talk was the conduct of the new Mrs. Jarrett and her stepson, Wilbert. While old Mr. Jarrett was at home in bed, or with his books in his library, his wife and son were seen dancing at some of the hotels.

In 1910 the new Mrs. Jarrett persuaded her husband to sell his wholesale clothing business, and move to Florida. They settled at Clearwater and built a new house next door to where I lived at that time. I met Mr. and Mrs. Jarrett, Wilbert and the maid, Berta, for the first time when they moved in and had a housewarming. What I have already told you I was to learn later from Chicago folks who had known the Jarretts back in the Windy City. The rest of the story comes from my own knowledge.

I was in the automobile sales and service business in those days, and the Jarretts bought a new car from me about every other year until old man Jarrett died at the age of seventy - six. When the will was probated it was learned that he had left everything to Anna, and nothing to his son, Wilbert. However Anna made it known that Wilbert would be taken care of as long as he didn't marry, and continued to live with his stepmother. From that time on Wilbert was never known to have a date with any woman. Anna Jarrett kept a tight rein on him, and he knew that to offend her would mean being thrown out of the house with scarcely a dollar to his name.

Anna used to consult Wilbert about her investments, and usually took his advice, but she kept almost everything in her own name. Once in awhile she would ask me about buying or selling some automobile company stock, but I knew little about her affairs until Wilbert up and died when he was about seventy-two.

After her stepson's death Anna began to depend on me more and more. Every other day or so she'd come to the house, or to my office to ask about buying or selling some stock, or what to do about a leak in the roof, or a dripping faucet. The older she got the more she hated to spend money, and before long she had me as her official handy man—without pay.

One day she came into my office and asked me to draw up a will for her. I told her to go to a lawyer, but she said they would charge too much, and she knew I could do it just as well. Then she told me exactly how she wanted to dispose of her property upon her death. I gathered that

she was feeling the pangs of a guily conscience for one reason or another. What she wanted to do was to see that the
woman, Berta, was well taken care of as long as she lived,
and then the rest of Anna's estate was to be divided equally
among a number of charities. She mentioned The Salvation
Army, the Humane Society, a home for orphaned children,
the county home for the poor, and aid for the blind.

When I saw what good she intended to do with her
money I was willing to do what she asked of me. I went to
considerable trouble in drawing up Anna's will, and then
had a lawyer look it over at my expense. Anna wanted me
to be her executor, so I put down my name, and the president of one of the Clearwater banks, as co-executors under
bond.

Things rocked along for a few more years but I could
see that Anna was failing in both mind and body. You'd
hardly believe some of the things she did. One day she had
the hot water tank disconnected at her home, and sold it for
five dollars. She said it cost too much to keep water hot all
the time, and all the hot water she and Berta ever needed
could be heated in a teakettle.

About a year later Anna fell and broke or cracked a
number of ribs. The doctor insisted that she hire a practical nurse, as Berta was getting too old and feeble to care
for a woman of Anna's size, and do all the housework too.
A week or so later this practical nurse came over to our
house and opened up her mind.

"What kind of women are they, anyhow?" she asked
my wife and me. "You know what happened last Saturday
afternoon? Well, Mrs. Jarrett put a little cold water in the
tub, and poured in one teakettle of hot water off the stove.
She took her bath, then ordered Berta to take her bath
in the same water so the soap in the water wouldn't be
wasted. I thought that was the cat's tenth litter of kittens,
but you ain't heard nothin' yet.

"Berta took her bath in the same water, and then Mrs.
Jarrett turned to me. 'Helen,' she says, 'now you can take

your bath. There's lots of good soap in the water, and it's still plenty warm.'

"And did you?" my wife smiled.

"I should say not!" the practical nurse snorted. "I said I'd take my bath at home, but you haven't heard it all yet. When they found I wasn't going to take a bath in that dirty water, Mrs. Jarrett gathered up her underwear and made Berta get down on her knees and wash it in the bathwater. Imagine that! Mrs. Jarrett said it would be a shame to waste all that good, soapy water. I thought I'd heard everything then, but there was still a little more to come. After the underwear was on the line Mrs. Jarrett had Berta bail up a bucket of water out of the bathtub, and use it to scrub up the kitchen floor. She said it would have been a shame to have wasted all that good, soapy water."

Hearing this sort of prepared me for what was to come. A month or so later I witnessed something that was hard to believe. I had taken Anna and Berta to the super market for their weekly shopping, and when I parked the car in my driveway I found that the women had left a package in the back seat. I took it over, and when I walked into their kitchen I couldn't help laughing. It was a funny sight, yet pathetic.

Anna and Berta were sitting across from each other at the kitchen table, and they were bent over, busy picking the raisins from a big mound of raisin bran heaped on the table. I saw the empty raisin-bran boxes on the floor, or I wouldn't have known what they were doing.

"What goes on here?" I inquired.

"We're sorting out the raisins," Anna explained. "Berta stews them and we have raisins for breakfast every morning."

"What's the use of all this?" I asked. "Why didn't you buy a box of raisins in the first place?"

'Oh, they're too expensive," Anna answered. "We buy raisin-bran, and that way we get all these raisins for nothing."

By this time you can probably see that Anna Jarrett was beginning to get senile. Plenty of others saw it, too, and there were two members of the church Anna used to go to, who decided to do something to feather their scrubby nests. One was a widow named Lottie Faller, better known to many as "Snoops", and Mrs. Sadie Krumby, who also answered to the name of "Crummy".

These two characters put their heads together and began to scheme up a way to beat the poor, the orphans, and the blind, and get a big chunk of Anna's estate for themselves.

They began their campaign by taking Anna and Berta a pint box of the cheapest ice cream, or a slab of home baked pie. They made it a habit to call on the two old ladies almost every day, and they spent most of their time in trying to convince Anna that a person had a greater obligation to friends—especially those who brought gifts of ice cream and cake—than to a lot of undeserving charities.

The first I knew of these devious methods was when Anna asked me if I didn't think she ought to change her will, and leave her estate to people who had done things for her. That was when I began to put two and two together, and saw what Snoopy and Crummy were up to. After that I tried my best to keep Anna on a straight track, but what can a man do against the machinations of two greedy and ruthless women?

The next thing I knew Anna Jarrett had made out a new will. In one of her saner moments she told me what had happened. Snoops and Crummy had gone to a young lawyer and retained him to draw up a new will, in which they were to be the beneficiaries of Anna's estate upon her death. Then they trotted a naive and bewildered Anna down to the attorney's office, and told her to sign on the dotted line.

"I don't know if I did right," Anna told me, "but they said I had to do it or God would be mad with me."

I would have taken some action about the new will, but a new development came just then, and I thought I could outwit the two grabbing women. What happened was that Anna at last sold her big house and took Berta into a small apartment. Anna asked me what she should do with the thirty thousand dollars, and I recommened putting the entire sum in U.S. "H" bonds, which pay interest every six months. Anna left the matter in my hands, and when I had the bonds made out I had them put in the names of Anna G. Jarrett or Berta Krell. Thus the bonds would become the sole property of Berta if she lived the longest, as it appeared she would.

Anna's mind grew rapidly worse. Snoopy and Crummy were doing their utmost to turn her mind against me. They told her I was going to the bank and taking things from her safe deposit box—as if the bank would allow such a thing—and they told her I was trying to have her put in an asylum. Lord knows what else they tried to tell her. After each session with these two—let's call them witches —Anna would send for me, and I would find her crying and upset. I always managed to straighten her out—for the moment, at least—but what a job!

And then, by some hook or crook, the two women discovered how the Government bonds were made out, and they ran to their lawyer about it. He hurriedly drew up a short will and told them to get Berta alone, and make her sign it. The will he prepared simply stated that upon the death of Berta Krell, everything she possessed was to be given to the estate of Anna Jarrett. Thus the bonds would automatically go back to Anna's estate, and into the hands of the schemers.

When I learned of this—through Berta—I came near going to the County Judge and having the Court put a stop to the antics of the two unscrupulous female bandits. Then I thought of an easier way to circumvent them.

On the pretext of making certain the bonds were intact I got Anna to go to her safe deposit box, and while we were there I found the envelope containing the will Berta had signed. I gave the envelope back to Anna, and after a perusal of the bonds, I took her back home. The next day Anna fell down the kitchen steps, was taken to the hospital, and died during the night.

Berta became ill as soon as the funeral was over, and she died in the hospital about a week later. Snoopy and Crummy were now in their glory, and began to scheme up ways of spending or investing the monies coming to them. Then, to their utmost horror, they learned that the will signed by Berta was missing, and that all the proceeds of the Government bonds would go to Berta's heirs in Germany.

As you can imagine the old ladies were fit to be tied. They went to court and tried to have the bonds delivered to them, but the case was clear cut, and the judge ruled against them. You never saw two more dejected and bedraggled females in your life. And so the money went to Berta's family in Germany, and it was only right. It made up for the more than sixty years the woman worked and slaved for the Jarretts without pay. Once in awhile there seems to be a little justice in this world after all.

*   *   *   *

Don Barton fell silent, and the rest of us thought over the story he'd just told. Finally I spoke up.

"Look here," I said. "You told us that the woman, Berta, made a will leaving everything back to Mrs. Jarrett's estate, didn't you? Well, then, what happened to it?"

"That isn't hard to explain," Don chuckled at the memory. "The day I went to the bank with Anna, I slipped Berta's will into my pocket and gave Anna the empty envelope to put back in the safe deposit box. As soon as I was back in my office I made certain that I'd have the last laugh on those two female buzzards. What I did was to light a match and burn the damn thing."

The Coconut Palm —
Best Friend to Man

Time: The Past and Present. Place: Tropic Lands and Islands

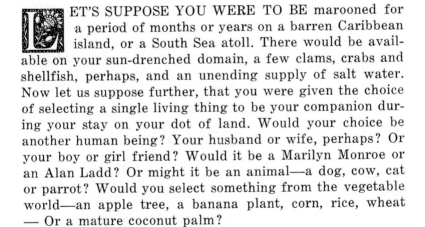 ET'S SUPPOSE YOU WERE TO BE marooned for a period of months or years on a barren Caribbean island, or a South Sea atoll. There would be available on your sun-drenched domain, a few clams, crabs and shellfish, perhaps, and an unending supply of salt water. Now let us suppose further, that you were given the choice of selecting a single living thing to be your companion during your stay on your dot of land. Would your choice be another human being? Your husband or wife, perhaps? Or your boy or girl friend? Would it be a Marilyn Monroe or an Alan Ladd? Or might it be an animal—a dog, cow, cat or parrot? Would you select something from the vegetable world—an apple tree, a banana plant, corn, rice, wheat — Or a mature coconut palm?

You would be wise, indeed, if you chose the coconut palm. Few people realize it but of all the Lord's creations the coconut palm supplies more of mans' basic needs than any other living thing on earth. Man can not live by bread alone, but he can live for long periods on the products of a single, mature coconut palm.

The common coco palm of the tropics, Cocos *nucifera*, is truly one of man's best friends. No other living thing in nature, be it animal, fish, fowl or vegetable, offers as many products or services to the human race. A single mature specimen of this palm will supply a human being with a constant supply of nutritious food, drink, rough clothing, shelter, fuel, and at the same time furnish the raw material for handicrafting such items as spears, nets, strainers, seives, brushes, matting, baskets, bowls and dippers, hats, thread, twine and rope. A form of crude sugar, and an intoxicating beverage called "arrack", are easily produced from the bloom of the coco palm.

A large coconut palm of plantation type can be expected to ripen and drop an average of one nut a day the year round. The heart bud of the palm is spoken of as "palm cabbage", and is a very savory salad-like food which can be eaten raw or cooked. The trunk or "log" of the fallen coconut palm contains thousands of tough fibres, and can be used for framing buildings, and constructing long lasting docks or piers. Sawed sections of coconut palm trunks are sold in Europe, and are known by the name of "porcupine wood."

The coconut palm has also acted as a teacher to the human race. Primitive man undoubtedly learned to weave cloth from viewing a section of coconut "cloth" when held up to the sun. This "cloth" which the palm manufactures to protect the young shoots from harm, consists of thread-like fibers forming both the warp and woof.

The home of the coconut palm is the entire tropical world, and in continental United States it is native and thrives only on the southern tip of Florida. The wide distribution of the palm is due to the nature of the fruit. The fibrous husk makes the nut very light for its bulk, and the leathery skin tends to prevent water-logging. Many coconuts lean over the water, and when the ripe nuts fall they float on ocean currents until they are washed up on some distant shore. Once imbedded in moist sand or earth on a tropic shore, the germination is usually quite rapid, and the nut sends roots downward and a green shoot skyward.

The coconut is the most useful of all the *Palmaceae*, or family of palms, and furnishes many valuable and important commercial products. It is the subject of careful cultivation in many lands. On the Malabar and Coromandel coast of India, for example, this palm is grown in huge numbers. On the Island of Ceylon where conditions are particularly suitable, it is estimated that there are 20 million coconut palms in commercial plantings.

The coconut palm furnishes the main exports of many regions. The kernels are pressed or boiled after being broken into small pieces, and are then dried in the sun. The dehydrated meat of the nuts forms the "copra' of commerce. One thousand large nuts will yield upwards of 500 pounds of copra, from which 25 gallons of palm oil may be had.

Coconut oil is a white, solid substance at ordinary temperatures, and has a peculiar and disagreeable odor. It is used extensively in the manufacture of candles, soap, cooking oils and margarine. This oil also finds some use in the production of synthetic rubber, hydraulic brake fluid, and safety glass.

During almost 40 years in South Florida I have grown a large number of coconut palms from seed, and have watched them grow into majestic specimens. There were a dozen or more matured coconut palms on my present home place when I took possession quite a number of years ago. My acre of ground was once a part of Thomas A. Edison's estate, and it may well be that the great inventor may have planted these palms with his own hands.

At this writing I have 36 coconut palms scattered over my grounds, and over the years I have grown and given away several thousand coconuts in the form of ripe nuts, seedlings, or well rooted plants. Even now, as I stroll day after day beneath the rustling fronds and curving trunks of my coconuts, I still have to marvel at the vast number of products and services they offer to mankind. To my mind they are the kings of the vegetable kingdom, and a best friend to the human race.

I have one word of warning for those who stroll or loll beneath stately coconut palms; that is to watch out for falling nuts. A mature nut filled with up to a quart of milk is a heavy object, and falls with considerable force. When I wander among my grove of coconut palms I usually take the precaution of protecting my head with a sun helmet. So far a falling nut has never hit me, but as a Cracker once told me, "You can't always sometimes tell."

A Whale of a Time at Naples

Time: 1936   *Place*: *Naples-on-the-Gulf*

I T WAS ALL MY FAULT, I'll admit. I should never have mentioned to the little woman that I'd once seen two big, live whales and a calf out in the Gulf of Mexico between Cuba and Yucatan. The word, "whale", it seemed, started her mind off on a single track. I'd seen a live whale; she wanted to see one, too. To her way of thinking it was just as simple as that. And it was up to me to produce a live whale for her inspection.

The time was over twenty years ago, and the wife and I were taking our summer vacation early. A rich man's widow had sold me a neat little cabin cruiser, the U-AN-ME, for a poor man's price, and I was anxious to try it out. We left Fort Myers in early June and spent a few days trying our luck with the tarpon in Boca Grande Pass. That was where I made the horrible mistake of mentioning the word, "whale".

I was sure, after I'd caught my first tarpon—a sixty pounder—that the mate would forget all about wanting to see a whale, but I was wrong as usual. She still remembered, it seemed, something from her Sunday School lessons, and she was bound and determined to see, first hand, what it was that gave Brother Jonah his chief claim to fame.

I cussed silently at the stupidness that had put this whale idea into her pretty little head. Then I realized that it wasn't altogether my fault; Old Man Jonah had had a hand in it too. Why in thunderation, I asked myself, could not the Old Boy have had his experience with a whale of a belly, instead of in the belly of a whale?

Of course I tried to argue the mate out of her "I-wanta-see-a-whale" idea, but I had very little luck. Well, to be perfectly truthful about it, I didn't have any at all. For a solid hour I tried to persuade the mate that a whale isn't such a hot spectacle, but a man eating shark, now—there's something worthwhile.

"I'm not interested in sharks," she came back at me. "They look like people, and all they do is loan money and charge high interest."

I saw I wouldn't get anywhere with that line, so I switched to another. "When we get down around Cape Sable," I promised, "I'll show you something real—a frisky barracuda." I went into considerable detail and explained that a barracuda had more teeth than a painless dentist's showcase, and was the *nee plus ultra* in deep sea fish. It was no use.

"I hate baritones," she snapped, "and I don't want to see any."

"You just wait until we stop at Sanibel Island," I said to change the subject. "This time of the year great big, giant sea turtles crawl up on the beach during the full of the moon, dig a nest in the sand, and lay as many as a hundred eggs. All you have to do is follow their tracks in the sand, scoop up a nice mess of turtle eggs, and . . . "

"So what!" the mate interrupted scornfully. "Who wants a lot of old turtle eggs? Besides, I've seen turtles. My sister used to keep one in a bowl with her goldfish. What I want to see is a live whale!"

Just about then I got a new idea and started on another track. I began to expound on the fact that a whale isn't a fish. A whale, I explained to the incredulous little woman, is neither fish, fowl or vegetable, but is a mammal—an animal. A mama whale, I said, is called a cow, and a baby whale is a calf, and the whales' calves get their infant eatments in the same manner as the calves on Uncle Oswald's dairy farm up near Chillicothe, Ohio.

"Oh, no you don't!" the mate exploded. "You can't think I'm that stupid! Why positively everybody knows that whales swim in the ocean. And the Bible says a whale is a fish, and whoever heard of anything but a fish living all the time in the water?"

The argument might have gone on for the rest of the day, but right then we made Bailey's dock on Sanibel Island, and we spent the rest of the afternoon stocking the larder, and taking on ice. After that we visited with friends until the small hours.

In the morning we decided to head south and visit Chokoloskee and Lostman's River, as we still had a few days left of our vacation. While we were passing off Fort Myers Beach a pair of frolic-some porpoises took up with the U-AN-ME, and began to use our bow wave as a sort of marine roller coaster. They would come from aft, arch their rubbery backs into the air, and then with a deep sigh dive out of sight. Inside of a minute they would reappear and repeat the performance. The mate was busy cleaning up after breakfast, and in a spirit of fun I called down into the galley: "Look!" I yelled, "Whales! Whales!"

I heard a clatter of falling dishes, then the sound of a cup or dish splintering on the deck. Then the mate's head appeared in the hatch. When she saw the playful porpoises she utterd a gasp of disappointment. There was a suspicion of tears, too. She'd seen porpoises before.

"I don't see a thing funny about it," she informed me grimly. "You know where there's plenty of whales—you're just trying to be mean. You just wait! I'll get even some-how!''

The rest of the morning and early afternoon was un-eventful. The Gulf was like a millpond under a lazy sun, and I kept well off the long string of verdant keys to avoid the bars and shoals. Every hour or so the mate would come to the cockpit and squint through the glasses. I could tell the whale idea was still on her mind, but I was thankful that she had calmed down somewhat. She went so far, once, as to admit that maybe whales weren't as plentiful as they used to be.

Along in mid-afternoon the little woman handed me the binoculars. "Look over there!" she pointed. "That must be Naples, but what are all those people and black things on the beach?"

I steadied the glasses against an awning support, and scanned the distant shore. I recognized the big hotel and the fishing pier, and then I saw them! The beach was alive with people, but what interested me was the black masses in and out of the surf. Even as I looked I saw one of the long, black objects give a convulsive shudder, and at the same time I caught a glimpse of the flukes of an oddly shaped tail.

"Whales," I shouted, and this time I wasn't fooling. About a mile north of the fishing pier there were at least forty or fifty of the sea-animals stranded along the beach by the outgoing tide. I remembered having read some-where that whales of the blackish variety, *globiocephalus melas*, follow a leader, and if the leader commits an error of navigation the whole school, or herd, follow him to their death.

In a short time I tied up inside Gordon's Pass, and we hitched a ride up the beach on a truck. When we drew near we saw an appalling sight of death, and near to death, covering a quarter mile of beach. Hundreds of thousands of pounds of flesh and bone sprawled in crazy patterns along the white sand. We took time to count the whales, large and small alike. There were fifty-seven of them. I took some pictures and paced the length of several of the largest whales. They measured 8 good paces, or about twenty-five feet. The babies were about ten feet long.

"How wasteful Mother Nature seems at times," said the mate as we prepared to leave.

"Well, matey," I said after we had returned to the U-AN-ME, "you got to see a whale — are you satisfied now?"

"I'm sorry for the poor things," she answered, and shook a tear from her cheek. "I almost wish I hadn't seen them." Then, womanlike, she did something I hadn't expected. She swung an arm around my neck and planted a moist kiss on my cheek. "That," she explained afterward, "is for letting me see what a whale looks like. I bet you knew where they were all the time."

I let it go at that. There was no use in starting another argument.

Bradenton's Bad Boy

Time: 1908 - 1932   *Place*: *The Bradenton Area*

ARRY STROUT WAS THE YOUNGEST child in a family of three boys and a girl, and he was a problem from the time he could walk and talk. He was born near New Port Richey in 1896, but when he was five the family moved south to what was then called Bradentown—before they persuaded the Post Office Department in Washington to drop the "w" and simplify the name of Bradenton.

The father of the family, Homer Albert Strout, became a constable of sorts, and from then on was generally spoken of as "Old Man" Strout. He was well liked and respected by all the better element of the community where he lived. That he had a son like Larry was deplored by most people living in and near Bradenton. Those in the know had a still greater sympathy for Mrs. Daisy Strout, and often wondered out loud how she managed to put up with the boy.

The other two Strout boys and the girl, Helen Marie, were never a source of anguish to parents or town, and hence have no place in the rest of our story. The same can not be said for Larry, for during his rather short life from cradle to grave he created enough strife and turmoil to

39

fill several books. That he didn't send his mother to an untimely death is still spoken of as one of life's little mysteries. As it turned out she stood by him to the bitter end, and lived to have a neat stone erected over his grave in the family plot.

Larry Strout began his pranks before he was well out of the cradle, but the first of his long line of peccadillos to be remembered by his family and neighbors, especially by the Goodling family who lived next door, happened when the boy was eight. It had to do with an alligator the boy found floating near the south bank of the Manatee River. The 'gator—a six footer—had been shot some days before, judging by the bloated condition.

The poor 'gator was very, very dead when little Larry hauled it from the water and loaded it on his little express wagon. It had been dead a great deal longer before John Goodling discovered what had driven his family out of their home, and caused them to spend a day and a night at the home of a relative.

Mr. Goodling and Larry's father, with handkerchiefs over their noses, had to tear up a section of the kitchen floor to remove the decomposed 'gator from the narrow space under the house. How a small boy of Larry's size could have shoved the carcass under the Goodling foundation all by himself was hard to believe, but the boy insisted he had accomplished it alone, with only the aid of a fence post.

When one of the nearby neighbors who had suffered from the horrible odor when the breeze was in the right quarter, remarked that nothing smelled worse than a dead 'gator, young Larry Strout had a quick and ready answer.

"Two real dead 'gators," he insisted, "would make a still better stink."

Larry had sharp ears and not only heard all the gossip going on over back fences and in his mother's kitchen, but he remembered everything he heard. When he was about the age of ten he began to make use of some of this information. Larry began to write notes and leave them under peoples' doors, or in their mail boxes. These notes, all written in a disguised scrawl, told of such things as what one neighbor had said about another; what man was calling at what house when the husband wasn't home, and extending invitations to call, or making dates to meet at another neighbor's house.

Of course the people in the neighborhood soon came to realize that the messages were fakes, done as a prank, but nevertheless it caused quite a stir in certain circles for a time, and caused more than one citizen to be more circumspect in his or her habits. There came a day when Larry was caught in the act of pushing one of his notes through a hole in a living room window screen, and the game was over. When "Old Man" Strout and Larry came from their informal meeting in the stable-shed in back of the house, the boy was changed in at least one respect. Thereafter he hated the sight of a pencil and never again bothered to do any writing that wasn't absolutely necessary.

When he was twelve Larry learned some of the simple facts about electricity. Electric lighting had come to the neighborhood where the Strouts lived several years before, but it took awhile for Larry to get around to sticking his finger inside an empty light socket when the current was "on". The resulting shock was not a bit to the boy's liking, but it gave him an idea for a new prank. He tried it on his sister first, and when he heard the scream she uttered he knew he'd found pay dirt.

Indoor plumbing had not yet arrived in the Strout neighborhood in that year of 1908, and as a consequence there was in the far rear of every yard a small outbuilding built and designed with but one purpose in mind. A few of the more ornate structures boasted of a coat of whitewash, and a crescent carved in the door. It was to three or four of these outhouses that Larry gave his attention in the following weeks.

Somehow, by hook or by crook, Larry had come up with a sizeable roll of electric wire, and by running the twisted pair under bushes and along fences, he was able to conduct his experiments in human behavior at consider-able distance from his home. The only other equipment the boy needed was a hammer and a few slim finishing nails.

It was a simple matter for Larry to sneak into a neighbor's privy when the family was away for the day, and to drive a couple of nails into the seat a few inches apart. He would drive the heads almost flush, and then fasten his electric wires to the pointed end of the nails where they protruded under the seat and out of sight. After that all he had to do was to connect the other ends of the wires to the nearest source of electric power. That, and listen for results as soon as the folks came home.

Several of the neighbors, furious at such indignities to their persons, traced the wires and made an accurate guess as to the perpetrator. After that there was another session in the stable-shed behind the Strout residence, and Larry turned his talents from electricity to girls.

Larry was about fourteen and a half when the father of a neighborhood girl came to see "Old Man" Strout one evening. His daughter, he explained in a strained voice, was pregnant, and Larry was to blame. When Larry was called in he didn't bother to deny it. In fact he seemed rather pleased that he had been able to seduce a girl about two years older than himself.

The girl's father made one thing plain right from the start. He didn't want any marriage bells; he didn't want anything as troublesome as young Larry for a son-in-law. The disgrace, he figured, would be bad enough as it was. There wasn't any sense in making matters worse by having a good-for-nothing, no account kid coming into his family. All he wanted was for "Old Man" Strout to help out with the doctor bills and provide a reasonable fund for the coming grandchild's keep. Larry's father realized it was an easy way out of a bad bargain, and he made haste to oblige.

At age sixteen Larry Strout was jailed for drunkenness for the first time, but it happened fairly often after that. He wasn't mean when he was drunk, but he did fill the air with profane words and delighted in singing ribald songs.

Larry was eighteen before he got into serious trouble with the law. It was over what happened at a dance out on an old wooden pier over the river. The dance had hardly begun before the girls and young women began leaving for home in pain and humiliation. It was a hot summer night and all had worn their sheerest dresses with not much on underneath. How were they to know, when they sat on the rough plank benches, that some prankster had smeared oil of mustard on the board seats. The resulting blisters on female posteriors kept every doctor in town busy through the night and well into the next day.

Of course the police were called into the case, and it didn't take them long to visit all the local drug stores and find out who had been around to buy a bottle of the mustard oil. As had happened before, "Old Man" Strout promised to pay all the doctor bills if the case against his son was dropped, and he was able to get two of the doctors to give him a wholesale rate.

In 1917 when he was twenty-one Larry enlisted in the army to help fight World War Number One, but he didn't last long. At the end of two months he had caused so much trouble in his training detachment, that they gave him a medical discharge and shipped him back home. It seemed that even in the army they wanted a little peace and quiet after a hard day on the march or drill field, and they couldn't get it with Larry there to keep things on the jump.

The ex-soldier had only been home a week when he was in trouble again. This time it was because he had painted the front of a young lawyer's office, doors, windows—everything—with a gallon of the yellowest paint imaginable. Why? Because the young lawyer who was single, had claimed his mother as being a dependent in order to keep himself out of the draft. Everybody, it seemed, but the members of the draft board knew that the lawyer's widowed mother was well fixed—almost rich, in fact. This time sentiment was on Larry's side, and when the police found yellow paint splattered on Larry's shoes, they let him off with a reprimand and his promise to pay for removing the paint.

By the time Larry Strout was twenty-three he had been married to three girls, one from Lakeland, one from Arcadia, and one from his home town. There was a wee bit of excuse for the out of town girls for they didn't know his background, but the local floosie went into the marriage with her eyes open. She took him "just for the kicks" she said on the day they were married, but three weeks and four drunks later the girl had enough of being Mrs. Larry Strout and moved to Tampa—permanently.

In 1920, when Larry was twenty-four, he became involved in a knife fight at a football game, and the three-inch cut between his mouth and left ear did nothing to improve his looks. He had been shifty looking, even as a boy, but with the livid scar added to the lines of his thin face he was positively ugly. In Hollywood he could have done well as a character actor specializing in prison riot scenes.

It was in this same year that Larry perpetrated what was perhaps his greatest prank. At least it caused an uproar and kept the police and sheriff's men in a tizzy for almost a week. On the first day of hunting season Larry and four companions were all set for a week-long stay in the woods. The old topless hunting car — a disreputable Model T — was all packed with food and gear, and the party were about to take off when Larry came up with an idea to get even with the cops.

The other young fellows listened and readily fell in with Larry's plan. In an alley behind the business section one of the pranksters filled his mouth with tomato catchup, then walked to a main street crossing and waited. Larry drove the hunting car around the block, and seeing that there were no members of the police in view, signaled to the one with a mouthful of catchup. This worthy then stepped off the curb in the path of the approaching hunting car, and staged a fake accident. As he went down under the front of the Ford he spewed catchup over his face and shirt front, and lay as still as death.

Larry and the other boys in the car leaped out and pretended to be thoroughly scared by the fake accident. One of the fellows fell to his hands and knees and placed his ear over the "victim's" heart.

"He's deader'n all hell!" he blurted out loud enough for a group of startled pedestrians to hear. "What do we do now?"

"Throw him in back," Larry ordered, "We'll dump him out in the woods somewhere!"

Several pedestrians tried to make themselves heard, but before they could get to a 'phone the boys had tossed the "dead" man into the back of the Ford, on top of all the camping equipment, and the rattletrap car went thumping down the street and out of town.

For the next few days the police and sheriff's men went hunting for Larry and his gang, and combed the nearby woods for the sign of a body, or a newly turned grave. It wasn't until the "dead" man returned to town (his identity had been established by several people at the scene of the "accident") that the law men finally had to admit that the whole thing was a joke on them. Behind their red faces was a sullen desire to get Larry, and get him good. In this desire they had almost a year to wait.

Larry's next brush with the law turned out to be the most serious one of his career. He became drunk and disorderly during a party at a house near Oneco, and when a Deputy arrived to take him to jail Larry was holed up in the garage beside the house, and he was well supplied with a rifle and revolver, and plenty of ammunition. After dodging a few close shots the Deputy sent for help, and the battle lasted all night. No one was killed—or even nicked—for drunk as he was, Larry was not vicious, and only aimed to keep the officers down behind several trees and a car in the driveway. He didn't want to kill anyone; just have a little good, clean fun. When morning came Larry's father walked into the garage, and brought his son out by the scruff of the neck.

The father's plea, a sharp lawyer and a sympathetic judge narrowed Larry's prison term down to six months, and the jailer was heard to comment that he was never so glad to lose a guest as he was to open the door and see Larry down the steps. It seemed that Larry had kept the jail in an uproar, day and night, with his ribald songs, profane jokes, and squirting water on all who passed in the corridor outside his cell.

During the height of the 1926 real estate boom Larry found a way to gather some quick and easy dollars. He became a bootlegger. Rumor had it that he bought moonshine from a man who had a still deep in Rattlesnake Hammock, and paid small boys up to 25c each for old whiskey bottles found on dumps, or gathered in family woodsheds. Some oak wood, half burned in an open fire, was then boiled in swamp water, and the resulting deep brown liquid was added to the 'shine to add the aged-in-the-wood taste and color. When the doctored 'shine was corked inside the famous name bottles it brought as much as $5 a quart, and showed a handsome profit. Success took it's toll, however, for Larry drank up or wasted every cent he made, and by 1930 he had developed a hopeless case of t.b.

Just before the end came Larry was loafing at the railroad station one day when the Tampa train arrived. He saw a man step down from a day coach; a man with a horribly scarred face, red streaked and blotched as if from a fire or acid bath. Larry hitched up his trousers on his shrunken frame, and walked up to the stranger. He brought his hand down on the man's back—hard.

"You poor bastard!" Larry said out loud. "At last I've done seen me a man who's uglier than me."

The stranger stepped back in surprise and took time to look into Larry's face. Then a slow smile came to the man's twisted lips. "I see what you mean," he said, "and I don't blame you a bit."

Larry died in 1932, and his mother, loving to the end, used some of the family's limited funds to have a neat stone placed over his grave. It read:

LARRY BEVAN STROUT
1896 — 1932
The Boy Who
Never Grew Up

'Davis Did It'

Time: 1925 - 1926   Place: Sarasota

BERTRAM DAVIS WAS A GOOD LOOKING young man. He had yellow - blond hair with a natural wave, eyes that were very blue, a generous mouth, a soft drawl, and polished manners. He had been born in the year 1900, and since our story opens in 1925, you can figure his age for yourself. Bertram—half the people in town called him "Bertie" to his face—earned his living as a clerk in Sam Wilson's small town department store, and he spent more than half of his time in the Ladies Shoe Department.

"Best darn clerk I ever hired," Sam often told some the boys at the Elk's Club. "It beats all how the girls—yes, and a lot of the married ones, too—fall for Bertie and his big blue eyes. You know, when he gives 'em that calf-love look of his you can see 'em almost melt. Why I'll bet half the girls come in just to have him hold their ankles while they're trying shoes, and to listen to the line he hands 'em. I'm paying him twenty-five a week, and he's worth every penny of it."

Bertie Davis might have gone on selling shoes without interruption if it hadn't been for one thing, and that one thing was real estate. All of a sudden vacant lots that had

49

hardly been worth the taxes began to sell. Land far out in the pine woods that had gone begging at fifty cents an acre —without the timber—suddenly began to sell for as much as a dollar.

"It's them Yankees," said some of the old time Crackers. "It's fellows like that Barron Collier from New York— they got so much money the banks won't keep it all, so they have to put it in land. Shucks! Them subdivision lots and that wild land ain't worth no more today than it was a year ago. Things has gone crazy, is what I say."

The Crackers may have been right, but the Yankees continued to come, and they brought money with them. Suddenly everybody, Cracker and Yankee alike, began to buy land. They didn't care if the price seemed high, for they knew that within a short time someone else would take it off their hands at a still higher price. It wasn't long before there weren't enough real estate agents to go round, so some of the newcomers and some of the old timers took out a real estate dealer's license, and rented desk space in an office or back room. Everybody figured to get rich by buying and selling to each other, and it beat working for a living by a long shot. And the beauty of it was that you didn't have to have much money to start with. All you needed to get your hands on a parcel of real estate was to put ten percent of the price down as a binder. Then all you had to do was sell it for a higher price before the option ran out, and put the profit in your pocket.

To everyone's surprise, even Bertie Davis got the real estate fever. He had saved up a matter of some fifty-odd dollars, and he put fifty dollars down as a binder on a vacant lot. Inside of a week he sold his binder to a man from Ohio for a hundred dollars profit, and turned right around and put the hundred and fifty down as a binder on a boulevard lot. Before the month was out he sold his interest in the boulevard lot, took a $400.00 profit on the deal, and quit his job with Sam Wilson to go into real estate full time.

"I'd've had to fire him anyway," Sam told the boys at the Elk's Club. "Bertie got so wound up in real estate he couldn't keep his mind on shoes, or catering to my women customers. Fact is, money's gone to his head."

Sam's observation turned out to be right. Money did go to Bertie's head, and since he made a lot of money in the next year and a half, he ended up by making a big fool of himself. He made one deal after another, and before the town really knew what Bertie was up to, he had bought a huge tract across the river, and was getting ready to open it up as Davis City. To get the palmettoes grubbed off quickly he offered a dollar an hour for common labor, which was twice the prevailing scale, and soon had a corner on the labor market.

When Bertie put his Davis City lots on the market he ran full page ads in the newspapers, and at the bottom of each ad, in bold letters three inches high, he ran three words that were to become his catch phrase—D A V I S D I D I T ! ! ! The whole town soon became sick of seeing "DAVIS DID IT!!" on billboards and posters, but it sold lots.

Of course Bertie and his flock of lot salesmen sold the lots on ten percent binders, but when the total contract prices were added up it came to a very impressive figure —on paper, that is. It was reported at the time that if all Bertie's lot buyers paid up in full, he would have over a million dollars profit.

As fast as the money came in, however, Bertie bought more land at inflated prices, with just a little down, and planned to develop more and better subdivisions, complete with golf courses and yacht basins. Before long the whole county was plastered with signs bearing the slogan, "DA-VIS DID IT!!"

In mid-summer of 1926 when the Florida land craze was at its height, Bertie Davis did two things he had never done before. He bought a new Packard automobile, and he hired a uniformed chauffeur to sit behind the wheel. Thereafter, between the hours of four and five in the afternoon, when all the real estate salesmen were wont to gather at the curbs up and down Main Street to make deals or compare notes, our friend Bertie would sit in the middle of the back seat of his black and glossy Packard, with arms folded across his chest, and spend the hour being driven up and down the main business streets of the town. It was an impressive sight, to say the least.

One day when there was an unusually large gathering of lot salesmen, mostly garbed in golf knickers (called "subdivision pants" by the uncouth of that era) as the badge of their profession, who should come trudging along Main Street in full view of the multitude, but an overly fat and bulging colored woman. One glance was sufficient to inform one and all the colored lady was but a few days away from the coming of a blessed event.

As usual there was a wag in the crowd, and at first sight of the lady of color, he put his hands beside his mouth and shouted at the top of his voice, "D A V I S D I D I T !" Everyone looked startled for a moment, but then they caught on and a huge roar broke from the crowd.

There is little more to tell about Bertie Davis. The boom broke shortly after, and his pyramided "deals" came tumbling down like a boulder on a mountain side. The profits he had made had been spread thin in acquiring options on other lands, and with the market gone he lost on every side. Squaring his debts took everything he had; even the Packard had to go.

Six months after the boom collapsed Bertie was back at his old job of fitting shoes, and to his credit let it be said that he took his come-down like a true sport. Once more he was able to turn on his charm when the ladies of the town came in for slippers, and people claim to have seen him going around on Sundays, in a dented Model T, busily taking down signs from land he no longer owned or had under option. The signs, of course, were the ones that bore the legend, DAVIS DID IT!!!

"Best darn clerk I ever had," Sam Wilson told the boys at the Elk's Club. "He never talks about the time he was a near millionaire—seems to have plumb forgot it. What gets me is the way the girls—yes, and a lot of married ones, too—fall for Bertie and his big blue eyes."

"Wild Life"
Along Florida's Suncoast

Time: The 1920s   *Place: Lee County*

WAS A YOUNG FELLOW, stone broke and looking for adventure when I left home in the North shortly after a hitch in the 1918 army, and headed south. By the time I reached South Florida I had exactfifty cents left to my name, but I wasn't worried. I had a small kit of tools with me and the day I arrived in town I landed a job. It wasn't much of a job; just doing some repair work for a man who owned a store, warehouse and several apartment buildings. He paid me $5 a day for carpenter work and allowed me to sleep in the warehouse.

A few weeks later I obtained steady work with a local contractor and, with my future more or less assured, I sent for the girl who was willing to share life's rewards and tribulations, and we were married by the County Judge in the Courthouse. It is one marriage which has stood the test of time—forty years—and is still going strong.

Of all the men in my crew, the one I liked best was a German named Adolph Etzwieler. He was not only a master carpenter, but he was well read and could speak intelligently on almost any subject you could mention—medicine,

botany, zoology, history, geography and the like. He had
in his youth traveled around the world in the German Mer-
chant Marine, and I can best describe him by saying that
he was a mental jack-of-all-trades.

Adolph, his wife and daughter, Agnes, lived in an un-
finished four-room house on the bank of a creek on the
edge of town, and one Sunday, a few months after my marriage, my wife and I called on the Etzwielers. To my surprise I found that Adolph had constructed a half a dozen
aquariums from cypress lumber, with glass on two sides,
and had them well stocked with varicolored tropical minnows he had collected in nearby waters. When I showed
more than passing interest in his hobby Adolph took pains
to enlighten me on the habits, care and feeding of his pets,
and loaned me several books on the subject.

Armed with the information the Dutchman had given
me, I used my spare time in making several aquariums of
my own, and borrowed a fine mesh dip net to stock my
tanks. I soon had a thriving and apparently happy group
of little fishes looking to me for board and room, but I
was far from content. Adolph had given me the name of
a tropical fish breeder in New Orleans who specialized in
exotic fishes gathered from the four corners of the world,
and I could hardly wait for the dealer's price list to arrive
so I could send him an order.

When the price list did arrive I sat down and placed
an order for a few Mexican Swordtails, Danios and Siamese
Fighting Fish. At the time I could ill afford to spend the
money for such a purpose—it was a matter of ten dollars
—but as you shall see it turned out to be one of the wisest
investments I ever made.

In a few days the expressman delivered my fancy fish,
and the postman brought a letter from the fish dealer in
New Orleans. He stated that he could use a few hundred
Holbrooki, and a few dozen pairs of Black Mollenisia, both
of which are native to South Florida streams. He offered

10c each for the little Holbrooki; a dollar a pair for good Black Mollies, and asked if I was interested?

I was not only interested, I was thrilled! For the next ten days I spent every spare hour out in the woods, walking along creek or canal bank, gathering Holbrooki and the harder to find Black Mollies. I shipped my first consignment to New Orleans in two 10 gallon cans, and about a week later I had the New Orleans dealer's check for something that had cost me nothing. I kept on collecting and shipping until the dealer told me to stop as he was over supplied.

I hated to lose my market for I had really enjoyed my collecting trips into the woods and tried to do some hard thinking. I reasoned that there must be others, besides the New Orleans man, who would be willing to pay me for gathering and shipping Florida tropical fishes. All I had to do was to get in touch with the right people. I mentioned my plight to Adolph and found that he had a ready answer to my problem. He loaned me a few back copies of an aquarium magazine, and the back pages were filled with ads wanting to buy or sell tropical fishes, goldfish, and all kinds of fish food, air pumps, water heaters and other aquarium supplies.

In about a month my own modest ad appeared in the magazine, and it immediately brought orders and requests from a number of dealers and individuals. Business picked up and by the next spring my new hobby had become a business and forced me into making a quick decision. It was a case of having to turn down orders — and return checks and money orders — or quit my regular job with the contractor.

As you can imagine, my heart was with the out-of-doors life of a commercial naturalist, so I gave up my week day jobs, much to my wife's alarm, and went into business for myself. I have never had cause to regret it, for it gave me improved health, greater peace of mind and contentment, a larger income, and eventually in a round about way, it led to considerable success in the literary field in later years.

My ads soon made me well known in the aquarium world, and inside of two years I was besieged with requests for all manner of Florida wild life — snakes, all kinds; turtles, all sizes; plants, water, land and air types; alligators, crocodiles, snails, sea creatures, driftwood, cypress knees, rare foliage, and what have you? I had to turn down an order from the New York Aquarium for a full grown manatee, weighing perhaps as much as two tons.

By this time I had prepared a printed, illustrated price list, and the U.S. Bureau of Fisheries had mentioned my business in some of their bulletins. Money began to come in faster than I had ever dreamed of, and in short order I had to buy a light truck for my collecting trips, and to carry my express shipments to the railroad station. During the busy summer months I hired several 'teen-age boys to help carry my nets, collecting cans and water jug, and to aid in packing and shipping. We roamed the woods and swamps within a 50-mile radius of town, and with each passing day I learned a little more nature lore, and saw the good of a man being able to do just what he wanted to do.

In time I was doing somethings in rather a large way. I sold the common top minnow, *Gambusia affinis,* in 5,000 lots to state agencies to be used for mosquito eradication, and I sold under-water plants by the thousand to be used for planting on sandy bottoms with the double barreled idea of providing food for wild ducks and preventing the shifting of channels in tidal streams.

One of my good customers in those years was the Davis Dry Goods Co. of Chicago. They maintained a large aquarium at street level for advertising purposes, and the man in charge of the display later became the Director of The Lincoln Park Zoo. In later years I wrote a story about him and one of his tamed wild animals, and sold it to Reader's Digest for 50c per word.

I found the commercial naturalist business to be full of surprises—most of them pleasant. One day an order came from the renowned Boyce Thompson Institute of Plant Research at Yonkers, N. Y. Enclosed was a certified check for $100.00 for which I was to supply 5,000 stalks of Giant Vallesneria, a long ribbon-like grass that grows at the bottom of shallow, brackish bays in Florida.

The next morning I hired two boys at $1.00 each to help fill the order, then loaded the truck with a potato fork, a washtub, a bundle of old newspapers for wrapping, a large, stout wooden box, a hammer, tacks and several address labels. A dozen acres of the Giant Vallesneria covered a bay bottom two miles from my home, and we were soon there. While I waded waist deep to dig up the water plants, the boys sat on the shore and untangled the twisted roots as I floated the grass, a tubful at a time, to the beach.

The Vallesneria were counted fifty plants to the bundle, well wrapped, and stored in the box. When the 5,000 were all packed, I nailed on the lid, tacked on the labels, and delivered the shipment to the express office. Allowing a dollar for the use of the truck, and two dollars paid to the boys, the three hours of my time had netted me a cool $97.00.

It was the rapid growth of my business that eventually caused me to become a writer of short stories and novels. It came about in this way: From time to time I would find myself with an over-supply of this or that variety of tropical fish, turtle, snake or snail, and my method of moving the surplus at a profit was to sit down at night and write an interesting article about whatever it was I wanted to sell. The next step was to send the article to one of the aquarium or wild life magazines for publication. I never received pay for these articles, but in the same issue I would have an ad offering whatever it was I had written about. Then all I had to do was sit back and watch the orders come in. It worked nearly every time, and in a matter of a week or so I'd have the money in the bank instead of fish in the tank.

In time, as the business grew, and to my good wife's dismay, our house became a wild life farm. The entire porch and spare bedroom were stacked with aquaria to the ceiling, and the front and back yards were spotted with cement lined fish ponds. The two-car garage was filled with shipping cans and nets, as well as a few cages for poisonous reptiles. I kept the alligators, larger turtles and the dry land tortoises in a vacant lot behind my property.

Such conditions had been all right when I first entered into the wild life business but in time the town grew out and around me, and the new neighbors began to complain. In fact some were quite hostile as soon as they discovered that their small fry insisted in playing around my small but well toothed alligators and water moccasins. In time I had to choose between moving out into the country—a fairly big job—or going out of the wild life business.

I gave the problem a lot of thought. There was much to be said on both sides of the question. The writing I had done for the aquarium magazines had shown me the way to do articles for some of the national magazines, and I had already had one how-to-do-it book published. Several editors offered to buy a series of articles if I would devote full time to writing, and such well known magazines as Hearst's *Motor Boating, Short Stories, Detective Fiction Weekly, Real America* and *Railroad Stories* had published fact and fiction from my typewriter.

I was still wavering on the brink of a decision when one of my former customers came and offered to buy my movable equipment, exotic fishes and good will. He wanted to start up a business of his own in another city, and we quickly made a deal. He is still in business after all these years and, as far as I can tell, is doing very well.

A short time later I sold the home place for a healthy profit, built a new and better home in a favored location, and devoted my full time to writing and traveling. As I look back over the years I realize how much of my modest success is due to Florida wild life. Not the kind of wild life to be found along Florida's Gold Coast, but the real, down to earth wild life to be found in the woods and streams, swamps and beaches of Florida's Suncoast. I owe a lot to the little minnows, the 'gators, turtles and snakes, and to the cypress knees, the shells and the sea life to be found on Gulf beaches, back bays or oyster bars.

These things I have mentioned form the kind of wild life so many, many serious minded people are interested in. In thinking back I often give thanks to Adolph, the German carpenter, who did so much to get me started on a new way of life. He made it possible for me to become a naturalist of sorts, and then a selling writer. If I had my life to relive I could hardly do better than to retrace my own footsteps.

Overheard on a Green Bench

Time: 1958   *Place*: St. Petersburg

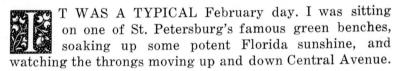T WAS A TYPICAL February day. I was sitting
on one of St. Petersburg's famous green benches,
soaking up some potent Florida sunshine, and
watching the throngs moving up and down Central Avenue.

Me? I was a "waiter"—waiting for my wife to dash
in and out of half a dozen stores, disturbing the merchan-
dise, bothering the salespeople, examining things she had
no use for, adding to the confusion, and buying a few odds
and ends which struck her fancy.

Two men—strangers by their conversation—were occu-
pying the other end of the bench. They began talking, as
visitors will, when the St. Pete brand of sunshine tempers
the cool breezes which drift across the peninsula from the
Gulf to Tampa Bay. I could do little else but listen.

"The trouble with this country," I heard the tall man
say, "is too much big business. You ever think of it that
way?"

Before the short, heavy set man could reply, the tall
man continued: "The giant corporations have it all their
own way. They stifle individual initiative on one hand,
and make it impossible for the little man to compete on the

63

other. Up in my country all that's left for the little man is to run a hamburger joint, a hole-in-the-wall newsstand, or try and sell some sort of gadget from door to door. It's either that or become a wage slave or hourly worker for some big outfit. There isn't any opportunities left for the little fellow."

"That may be true where you come from," the short man broke in, "but it doesn't apply here in Florida. When a place is growing like this state there's almost unlimited possibilities for a real go-getter. I know half a dozen young fellows in my town who've cleaned up in the last few years, and they did it from scratch. One was a young fellow who came over from Italy—couldn't speak a word of English when he arrived. He got a job as a machinist up in a New England factory, and at 40 cents an hour he managed to save enough by 1930 to marry and take his bride on a six month visit to Italy.

"In 1933 he was laid off, along with 4,000 other employees of the factory, and there were no jobs to be had in New England. It was then that Anthony Sarlo saw the light, and moved to Florida. He was soon at work as a blacksmith's helper, and he learned a lot more about working iron, welding and machine work. In a matter of a few years Sarlo bought the blacksmith shop where he worked, and all of the stock and equipment of another blacksmith who had died. In a short time he changed the name of his business to THE FORT MYERS IRON WORKS, and was soon doing a growing volume of designing and manufacturing ornamental railings, grills and stairs.

"During these busy years Anthony Sarlo had been busy acquiring land for a new venture which was growing in his mind. He had hardly completed his new and modern machine and welding shop when he was issued a United States Patent on a new and greatly improved power lawn mower. After the pilot models had been tried and perfected Anthony Sarlo built a new and modern factory building, fitted it out with the latest machine tools, and went into the mower manufacturing business on a large scale. In spite of the fact that Sarlo's mower sold for twice the price of many models put out by the big northern manufacturers, his sales grew year by year.

"In time Anthony Sarlo had to double the size of his plant as customers beat a path to his door. When their schooling was finished Sarlo's two sons, and a nephew, joined him in the business. Now the plant has a full time salesman on the road, and 14 employees. Last year Sarlo bought his wife a new Cadillac to go with the new ranch type house they live in on McGregor Boulevard. Besides all this Sarlo's business enjoys a good rating in Dun and Bradstreet, and sells about a quarter million dollars worth of mowers and parts a year. Now do you still say it's impossible for the little fellow to compete with the big corporations?"

"I don't see how he could do it," the tall man said after a bit of reflection. "I've got two sons in Pennsylvania and a nephew in Ohio. All have been through college but they're not doing so well. One of my boys works in an office, the other's the manager of a bowling alley. My nephew's got the best job of the three—he owns a small laundromat—and works about twelve hours a day to clear $7,000 a year before taxes. The Italian boy you spoke of must have had plenty of luck to do so well."

"I wouldn't call it luck," the heavy set man came back quickly. "This fellow, Sarlo, had sense enough to come south where the opportunities are, and he had brains enough to make a better mouse trap. The last time I was in Fort Myers I was talking with Anthony Sarlo, and I asked him a question.

"Why it is," I asked, "That you, a poor boy who came from Italy, have been able to make good when many an American-born boy, with no language trouble and all the advantages, are in second and third rate jobs and working for peanuts?

Anthony Sarlo smiled and took time to think it over. Then he looked me straight in the eyes. I could see that I'd caught him off guard. I guess no one had ever asked him that question before.

"Well," he said last, "I think maybe when you don't have a lot of education —" he paused to point to his right temple, "you just have to use your head."

Success at Sarasota

Time: 1920 - 1950   Place: Sarasota

 STILL REMEMBER THE DAY we rattled into town, and parked our Model T in the shade of an oak tree. The town looked better than most we'd seen on our way south; the streets were cleaner, and the stores and buildings looked more modern. I turned to my girl-wife—we'd been married almost a month—and said, "This is it! Here's where we're going to hang our hats! I'm hungry—come on, let's hunt a place to eat."

We were young then—I was just twenty-four—and the fact that we were on speaking terms with poverty didn't worry us one bit. In the back of the flivver were my auto mechanic tools, and in my watch pocket was a ten dollar bill to be used in case of emergency. I had another three or four dollars in my pants pocket, and Marie had some small change. I guess we knew — subconsciously — that if America was the Land of Opportunity, then South Florida was the Land of Promise. I wasn't long out of the World War I army, Florida had beckoned, and we had answered the call. It was all as simple as that.

After we'd had a bite to eat I left Marie to watch the car, and I set out to hunt a job. I planned to work a few months in a local garage, save up a little money, and get the lay of the land. When the right time came I intended to start a repair bsuiness of my own. It all seemed so easy at the time.

"Sorry, buddy," said the boss of the first place I visited. "I'm firin', not hirin'. See me 'bout next December—when the tourists start comin'."

I tried the Ford agency next. "Nothing doing, son," said the white haired shop foreman. "Can't keep the boys busy the way it is. The summers are slow down here. Yes, and mighty l-o-n-g, too."

The third place I tried was on a side street. The two owners were sprawling on a bench out front. When I asked for a job they both laughed.

"Look," said one, "if we had even one job in the shop do you think we'd be loafing out here?" Suddenly his partner straightened up. "If you want to buy a business, we'll sell for five hundred—cash."

There was still one more shop to try. It was about the oldest garage in town, and the proprietor was old and white headed. He tried to let me down easy.

"I never take on new help," he informed me rather sadly. "I got me two good mechanics—had 'em both for years—they're all I ever need."

"But," I said in wonder, "doesn't your business grow?"

"Nope," said the old fellow. "It stays 'bout the same all the time. You see as the town gets bigger other shops start up, and I keep 'bout the same customers year after year."

I was beginning to get the picture, and it didn't look so good. However, some of the confidence of youth was still with me, and I wasn't downhearted yet. The last fellow had pointed the way I'd have to take; start a shop of my own. But with what? I had no money to rent a building, and buy lumber for benches, signs and shelves. Anything in the way of starting a new business would have to be done on trust.

On the way back to where Marie was waiting in the car, I passed a warehouse where they sold groceries, feed and fertilizer, and an idea came. There was a lean-to building beside the warehouse, once evidently used as a wagon shed and stable, and it could be turned into a garage with a little work. I located the owner of the business, and within half an hour we'd made a deal. I was to have the use of the lean-to building, and he would take the first six months rent out in repairwork on his delivery trucks. In addition he promised to lend me several of his men to help clean and paint the place, and to mention me to his customers.

I hurried to tell Marie of the good news, and to start looking for a place to live until we got on our feet. On the way I had visions of myself having to work overtime, and I could picture a fast growing bank account. In the near distance I imagined I saw a neat cottage with flame vines on the roof, and orange trees in the yard. Everything seemed to be almost within reach.

Disillusionment came slowly. I had expected to be busy almost from the start of my new venture, but my optimism proved to be misplaced. Aside from repairing one of the landlord's trucks against the rent I owed, I had little to do. For some days the only thing to break the peace and quiet of my shop were a few horseflies, drawn by the lingering smell of harness and mules.

We were down to our last single dollar, and I knew if something didn't happen soon I'd have to sell the Ford to keep on eating a little longer. I was feeling low, and as a last resort I knew I'd have to let Marie's folks send her the money to go back home until I got on my feet. Suddenly my thoughts were interrupted as a long, black car rolled into my little shop. No, it wasn't a car, I saw, it was a hearse! I hurried to the driver's side and looked in.

The man I saw there was all of six feet, and rather

heavy set. He was scowling at me through thick lensed, black framed glasses. "So you're this new mechanic!" he half muttered. "Hum! You're kind of young—but no matter. All the other gyps have taken me to the cleaner—you might as well have your chance."

The undertaker crawled from under the wheel with a grunt, and gave the front tire an angry kick. "I sure bought a lemon," he told me. "She does all right up to 40 miles an hour, then begins to backfire and cut-up. Everybody in town's had a crack at her—they've tried new points, new distributor, new carburetor, and a new set of plugs. One shop said it was dragging brakes. Hell! The only thing the boys haven't tried is to paint her red! You know what? She's cost me all the profit on four good funerals—and I've still got the same complaint. Besides, it made me too late at two accident cases. One of the birds died, so I lost a funeral, too. You want to take a crack at her, young fellow?"

I don't remember what I said. For the moment I was overwhelmed by the suddenness and the importance of the job. I lifted the hood, tried to look wise, and began to check everything I could think of.

I didn't know it at the time, but Jim Kreep, the undertaker and his new "meat wagon"—as some of the natives called it—had become the joke of the town. A rival undertaker, Mr. Berry, had started business the year before, and both men were fighting for all they could get. Thinking to outsmart the new undertaker, Mr. Kreep had gone into debt to buy the newest modern hearse, but because of the balky engine he was worse off than before.

You know how small towns are. It didn't take the storekeepers, clerks and bench sitters along the main drag long to spread the word about the backfiring ambulance-hearse. They knew that Berry's broken down hearse-ambulance, converted from an old limousine, had outrun Kreep's deadwagon to several highway accidents, and everytime Mr. Kreep stuck his nose outside his funeral parlor, some wise guy would yell, "BANG! BANG! BANG!" He'd had about all the ribbing he could stand.

Well, I took the hearse out for a test run on the highway, and Mr. Kreep went back to sit beside his telephone —just in case. The engine acted just like he'd said it did. Up to about 40 it was smooth, but over 40 it sounded like Benny's Maxwell. Hum-hum-pft-pft-bang-bang-hum-hum-pft-pft-bang-bang-pft-pft—was the way it went.

Back at the shop I checked everything between fan and flywheel. I couldn't find a thing wrong with compression, timing, points, plugs or carburetor. Yet it had to be somewhere, or in something. Then I looked at the ignition coil and was sure I'd found the trouble. It was the same model coil as used on small four cylinder jobs, and this was a high speed eight.

I went to the biggest garage in town and talked them into letting me have a high speed coil on credit. When it was installed I took the hearse on another test run, and the trouble was gone. Hearse or no hearse, I sang out loud all the way back to the shop.

When I presented Mr. Kreep with my bill he paid it without a murmur. He did a lot more than that. He became my unofficial service salesman. He never missed an opportunity to mention my shop, and give me a big boost into the bargain. Within a week or two I had all the business I could handle, and I went on from there. Customers would come around and ask, "Are you the fellow who fixed the hearse?" or, "Are you the guy Mr. Kreep told me about?"

Five years later I bought a lot and put up my own building. Right after that I took on a new car agency, and did right well. My business grew with the city, and after thirty years I sold the business but kept title to the real estate. Over the years I'd bought stock in some Florida utilities, like Tampa Electric, Florida Power, and Florida Power and Light, and today they're all worth three or four times what I paid for them, and bringing in a good income besides.

Now that I've retired from active business I can do a lot of the things I've always wanted to do. I have a fine woodworking shop; I've taken up oil painting; go fishing a lot; take a long summer trip to the Smokey Mountains, and have a little time left for reading, listening to the hi-fi, and watching television. If there were 48 hours in a day, instead of only 24, I'd still find a good use for everyone of them.

Today we live in a nice modern ranch house, my wife has a new Cadillac in her stall in the carport, we have a lot of congenial friends, an ample income for our needs, and up to the present all members of our family have enjoyed good health. Some people who know us often say that we haven't a problem in the world, but they are wrong.

In spite of all my blessings I do have a problem. It is my opinion that everyone has a problem of one sort or another. I am lucky that my problem isn't as serious as many people face. But I do have a problem, as I said before. To state it quite simply my problem is — What is my my problem? I wish Mr. Anthony of radio days was around to tell me the answer.

The Nurse From Mendigo Key

A PLAYFUL SUNBEAM speared through the open hatch as the *Bon Temps* swung at anchor, and made Cass Summers aware that it was early morning. He yawned once, stepped up to the deck, and looked around. Save for a fisherman's camp on a distant beach, the landlocked bay was silent and deserted. Cass stepped out of his shorts, jumped to the stern seat and dived into the greenish water.

For five minutes he swam slowly, making a wide circle around his cabin cruiser, then climbed to the cockpit and picked up a towel. If it hadn't been for his movements you'd have sworn he was a copper colored statue. His legs were sturdy, his arms well muscled, and his waist and hips were lean. His mouth was made to wear a ready smile, and even though wet, his brown hair displayed a tendency to curl. Cass Summers was all of twenty-eight, but he could have passed for twenty-three or four.

This was the life, he thought, as he whip-sawed the coarse towel across his back. Florida in February! Warm sun! Cool nights! Splendid fishing! Do as he pleased, with no women around to pester him morning, noon, or night. That, he told himself, was the part he liked best. Women? The heck with them!

Now Cass was really a sensible young fellow, and he tried to be fair about it. He didn't blame any girl for wanting security, a husband who'd stay home nights, a ranch house on a large plot, a check book of her own, and maybe some babies to fuss over. What he did object to—and with good reason—was the antics of the babes who'd been trying to grab him up. He was quite modest, so he figured they wanted a wedding band because he just happened to have a good income and money in the bank. He was sure they didn't want him just for himself.

When you know the facts you could hardly blame Cass for thinking as he did. While he was in the Air Force an aunt had willed him a sizeable fortune, and the news got around. When he returned to his home he found the local debs were ready and waiting for a trip to the altar. In fact they were positively eager.

To get away from the home town girls Cass went down to Miami, and for about a week he felt as free as the pigeons in Bayfront Park. Then it happened. A girl from back home spotted him in the lobby, and the chase was on again. For a whole day Cass remained locked in his room, and he studied the girls-with-a-marriage-complex business from every angle. Then an idea hit him!

A boat was the answer! Why hadn't he thought of it before? Once a fellow left the dock—alone—he was safe from the cute little schemers until he made port again. The idea, the more he thought it over, seemed to have merit. You recognize the theory . . . a man in his boat . . . alone against the sea . . . that sort of stuff.

He found the *Bon Temps* moored in the Miami River, and she was for sale. He fell in love with the craft at first sight. The price seemed high, but after a second look at the mahogany deck house, and the thirty-five feet of white hull, he signed a check and took over. Because the owner had decided to sell suddenly, the cruiser was fully stocked and ready to cast off.

Cass loafed southward among the keys for a few days, getting the feel of the craft and basking in the sun. Then he rounded Cape Sable and began to explore the wild region of islands, bays, and rivers on the west side of the Everglades National Park. The fishing was good, and at night he had some books and a radio. What more could a man ask for?

After a brisk rub-down on deck the young man swung into the cabin, and covered a part of his nakedness with a pair of boxer shorts. He next stopped in the tiny galley long enough to warm some stale coffee, and munch a bowl of soggy cereal. The larder was running low of staples; he'd have to stock up when he reached Fort Myers.

Cass was hauling in the anchor when he heard the put-put-put of a gas boat putting out from the fishing camp. There was a man standing in the launch, and he seemed to be waving. Cass dropped the anchor line and waited. When the weather-beaten craft drew near he was surprised to see a girl in the stern seat. The bare-footed fisherman choked his engine and brought the disreputable boat alongside.

"Hi, mister!" the man called out. He was a typical islander; patched overalls, unkempt hair, with watery eyes set in a stubble covered face. "Hit's goin't' be a nice day . . . . "

"Good morning!" interrupted the girl in the gas-boat. "I'm Ruth Jordan—just finished nursing this man's wife —give me a lift to the first town you come to, will you?"

Cass stood and looked down with his mouth half open. He came near saying, "No!" but he thought better of it. He stared at the young woman. She was is a uniform and wore what once had been white shoes and stockings. She looked sort of dirty and bedraggled, yet there was poise in her manner. She stood up and gripped the rail of the *Bon Temps*. Then before Cass could even offer his hand the girl had tossed a grip aboard, and jumped into the cockpit.

In spite of the soiled and wrinkled nurses' uniform, Cass could see that there was youthful symmetry to her body. He noticed, too, that even with her hair pulled into a tight and unbecoming knot, she was good looking. Darn good looking, and with not a bit of make-up.

"All right," Cass got around to saying at last. "Just where do you want to go?"

"Fort Myers," the girl answered promptly, "but you can drop me at Everglades or Naples—I can take a bus from there. I don't want to put you to any trouble."

"No trouble," Cass answered reluctantly. "I can have you in Everglades by noon—or a little after."

Cass frowned as he went forward to haul in the anchor. Why did the girl have to show up and spoil his way of life? Then he tried to reassure himself. It would only be for a few hours, and besides, she didn't look like the kind who'd make trouble.

The *Bon Temps* was well out into the open Gulf before Cass missed the girl. She'd gone down into the cabin soon after he'd started the engine, and she hadn't come back. He began to wonder if she was the snooping kind. Like women shoppers in department stores, who pick up stuff just to throw it down again. After a time he slid off the pilot's seat and peered down the hatch. For the first time since he'd left Miami the spare bunk wasn't littered with cast off clothing and books, and his own bunk was neatly made.

Then he saw her in the tiny galley. She was stacking dishes away in the locker, and a wave of guilt swept over him. He hadn't washed a plate, or a pot, or a cup for a whole week, and he was ashamed that she'd found the galley in such a mess.

"What are you doing down there?" he called out for something to say.

The girl's face appeared around the bulkhead. "Working for my passage, skipper," she sang out. "Everything's almost under control."

In a few more minutes the girl came from below and stood beside Cass. Neither spoke until the silence became awkward. He was the first to speak.

"How'd you happen to be down here?" he asked at last.

"It was an emergency," she stated simply. "The fisherman's wife was going to have a baby—there were complications—all the doctors were too busy—so I came."

"I see," Cass ventured. "You're with the Public Health Service?"

"No," the girl answered matter of factly, "I'm a nurse with a settlement house up north. I happened to be vacationing at a hotel in Fort Myers when I heard some people from a yacht tell about the poor woman on Mendigo Key. I hired a seaplane to take me down, and it was a good thing I did. Another day and the woman wouldn't have made it. S-o—here I am."

Cass felt a shudder creep up his spine. He could imagine the inside of a rough shantyboat; the frightened fisherman; the wife in labor, and no doctor within fifty miles. Then this young nurse drops out of the sky and takes over. Her coming saves a life; probably two lives. Some way to spend a vacation!

The girl glanced at her watch. "Want me to see what I can dig up for lunch?" she asked.

"You'd better," Cass half smiled. "Anything I'd cook up you wouldn't eat."

The best part of an hour passed. Suddenly Cass caught himself sniffing the air. An aromatic and tantalizing aroma was coming from the hatch. He rubbed his stomach hungrily. He found himself wishing it was time to eat. And then the girl's head and shoulders appeared, and she was holding a plate. And on the plate . . .? He could hardly believe his eyes. Cupcakes! Cupcakes with chocolate frosting.

Cass took a healthy bite from one of the cupcakes. The sides were golden brown, and the icing was still warm and soft. He crammed the rest into his mouth and reached for another.

"M-m-m, good!" he muttered. He looked around to find the girl gone. She was back in a moment with a cold Coke from the ice chest. He took a swallow, and downed another cupcake. "Swell!" he mumbled. "They're simply super!"

The cruiser was well off shore when the girl called him for lunch. He cut the ignition and allowed the *Bon Temps* to drift while he was below. He found redfish fillets, baked potatoes, hot biscuits, fresh coffee—and more cupcakes. He took seconds all around, and tried to study the girl as he ate. He had to admit; the girl was handy with a skillet. Once he began to think about how nice it would be to have a plain, sensible girl to sort of keep house for a fellow, but he gave a snort and put the idea aside.

He offered to help with the dishes, but she wouldn't hear of it, so he went topside and started the motor. An hour passed before he saw her again. The *Bon Temps* came even with Chokoloskee Island, but instead of turning in towards the town of Everglades, he decided to take the girl on up to Naples. It was about the least he could do, considering the way she'd worked over the cupcakes and the lunch. And cleaned up the cabin.

Thirty minutes went by. Then the girl stuck her head through the hatch. "Everything's shipshape below, skipper," she sang out. "Everything but me, that is. Mind if I take a shower?"

Cass told her where to find the switch that operated the fresh water pump, and she ducked below. He leaned over and closed the hatch—give the girl some privacy. How different she was from the girls back home. Capable and independent. Able to do things—earn her own living. She didn't have to hook some man for a meal ticket.

After a time the hatch opened and Cass could hardly believe what he saw. There'd been some changes made. The soiled nurse's uniform was gone, and so were the scuffed shoes and white stockings. Instead he saw sharkskin shorts, evidently taken from her grip, and one of his own oversize T shirts. Her feet were bare. She leaned over the rail to allow the breeze to help dry her hair.

Cass took time to study her wind-whipped profile. In spite of himself he had to admit that she was sweet and wholesome looking. And beastly healthy. It was all real, too. No make-up, no figure padding like you see offered for sale in stores and magazine ads. How different she was from the silly girls of the country club set back in his home town.

"Will we make Fort Myers tonight," the girl suddenly asked.

Cass took time to consult his chart rack. He had intended to put in at Naples and be done with his passenger, but now he wasn't so sure. Somehow the girl was starting to grow on him.

"The way we're going," he spoke at last, "we ought to make Fort Myers by seven tonight—or eight at the latest. What's the matter Cupcake, are you in a hurry?"

"Cupcake!" the girl laughed. "I've never been called that before."

The name had slipped off his tongue naturally enough, and it seemed to fit. He was glad she'd taken it as a joke. What was the difference, anyway? She was here today, and gone tomorrow. And then Cass happened to rub his chin, and it dawned on him that he must look like a tramp. He hadn't bothered to shave for the best part of a week.

"Hey, Cupcake," he called, "Take over for me, will you?"

The girl took his place and put her hands on the wheel. Cass stood as close as he dared, and showed her how to keep the compass pointing.

From her position on the pilot's seat, the girl's head was even with his own, and Cass couldn't keep his eyes from straying. He took in the short, silky curls at the nape of her neck, and then the delicately moulded pinkness of her right ear. His gaze wandered to the blush of her freshly scrubbed cheek, and then to the saucy tilt of her nose. Her eyes . . . ? He couldn't see them, but he remembered they were large and well spaced.

The girl seemed to sense that Cass was taking inventory. Her head turned suddenly and their faces were just inches apart. To a seagull overhead the situation looked promising. Her lips were slightly parted, provocative — and did he imagine it?—expectant as well. He found himself swaying nearer . . . nearer . . . but he managed to pull back in the nick of time. Wow! That had been a close one! He stammered an excuse and dived below.

Cass shaved and took a shower to cool off. When the came back on deck he was in slacks, T shirt and sneakers. And munching another cupcake. He checked the time, picked up the glasses, and scanned the distant shore.

"Fort Myers Beach coming up," he announced. "If all goes well I'll have you in Fort Myers by 8 p.m."

The girl didn't answer. There was a far away look in her eyes as she sat on the transom, with her chin on her knees. In about a half hour she got up and went below. Cass could hear her stirring around in the galley.

"What's cooking?" he called down.

Her head bobbed up for a moment. "I'm gettin' supper," she explained. "Have to earn my way, you know."

Cass did some thinking as he kept the *Bon Temps* headed for Sanibel Island Light. It was going to be different aboard after Cupcake left. Come to think of it, it might be fun having a girl like that around most of the time—one who was willing to pitch in, and wasn't after a fellow just for his money. That, he decided, was where the poor chap had it all over the rich guy. The poor chap could be sure the girl took him just for himself, and not for his bank balance. This Cupcake, now—she hadn't asked any leading questions; she hadn't tried to pry into his . . .

"What in the hell . . . ?" Cass barked aloud, as he heard the engine begin to slow down and backfire. He worked the throttle lever violently, but it did no good. The engine didn't quite stop, and he found it would still run smoothly if he kept the throttle almost closed—just limping along.

Cass left the wheel and dived below. He knew there was plenty of fuel in the tanks, so he started tinkering with the engine. He gave up after a few minutes.

"It beats me," he told Cupcake. "The ignition, oil pressure and fuel pump seem to be working, and there's plenty of gas. At this rate we'll be lucky to make the mouth of San Carlos Bay by dark. You know what it means? It means we'll be out all night."

The girl shrugged her shoulders. "If it has to be, it can't be helped," was all she said. She didn't seem concerned.

"Makes no difference to me," Cass retorted, "I was thinking of you. It might start people talking . . . "

"No one's checking on me," she stated. "And besides; who's to know?"

"Okay, then," said Cass. "We'll crawl behind Sanibel Island, and I'll get the engine fixed in the morning. You'd better hold up supper awhile."

It was well after dark when Cass dropped the anchor in back of Sanibel Island. He switched on his riding lights and went below. They lingered over supper for a time, then he insisted on helping with the dishes. This time he was firm about it.

The galley was small, but two could manage if they didn't mind bumping into each other. Of course it happened accidently. In reaching for a plate his lips almost brushed against Cupcake's cheek. Instinct forced him to act on the impulse. He gave her a quick peck of a kiss. It was poorly placed and not at all satisfactory. He made another try, but found himself fended off by her elbow.

"Wait," was all she said.

Cupcake snatched the dish towel from his hand, and he saw her wipe the suds from her wrist. He thought she was making ready to use her fists, and he drew back a little. Then Cass felt lightning strike! It took him an instant to realize that it was just her arms darting around his neck. The plate fell from his hand and smashed at his feet. His arms closed around her waist and drew her close. This time the kiss was quite satisfactory, and it set off a chain reaction.

After a time they went to sit in the cockpit, and watched the revolving beam of Sanibel Light. They held hands and talked a little. Bit by bit he learned a few things about her. Her parents were dead, and she'd quit college to become a trained nurse. She was a little vague about it, but she had something to do with a nursing service for the poor —up north.

In between times Cass told her a little about himself. He mentioned his hitch in the Air Force, and said he helped run a television shop in New Jersey. He didn't bother to explain that the business sold several million dollars worth of electronic parts a year, and that he was one of the larger stockholders and president of the company.

Then Cass began to fumble around, trying to ask a question. He wouldn't have considered it, even an hour before, but now it seemed like a splendid idea. He got the question out at last, but he muffed the lines. It sounded pretty crude.

"Cupcake," he asked, "would you have a guy like me?"

It wasn't the way he wanted it to sound, but that's the way it came out. He was afraid she was going to laugh in his face.

Instead he felt her head turn against his shoulder. She snuggled a little closer. Then he heard her soft, clear voice close to his ear. "What do you think?"

There! It was over! As simple as that! He held her close, his practical mind already busy with plans. There'd be a new rambling house on a hill—with lots of trees, and swings for the kids. And Cupcake to come home to.

They would've sat there all night if it hadn't been for the sandflies. A shift in the wind brought a swarm of the vicious little insects, and they had to go below and close the hatch. They stretched out on the bunks, with the aisle between, and put out the light. It was hard to stay awake in the dark.

Cass yawned. "You're taking an awful chance, Cupcake," he muttered.

"Chance?" she echoed. "How do you mean?"

"I mean falling in love like this. You don't know anything about me . . . "

"But I do!" the girl said. "I didn't know who you were when I came aboard, but I saw some envelopes addressed to you when I straightened up the cabin. You're Cass Summers, president of Shermann Electronics, Incorporated, and I know a lot more. You see, Phyllis Bates is my second cousin."

Cass almost fell out of his bunk! So Cupcake was related to Phyllis . . . Phyllis, one of the eager beavers back home who'd been trying to trick him into marriage. Phyllis, a little two-timer he'd had no use for. So that was the game! Cupcake had known all along that he was a young fellow in the chips—she was just another gold digger— as bad as her cousin, Phyllis.

"Oh," said Cass grimly, "I can see the angle now."

He felt like he'd been doused in cold water. Cupcake was just another girl ready to latch onto the first fellow with a bank roll. Baking the cupcakes, cleaning things up, cooking the meals, making herself alluring, kissing him like that, and fixing it so's they'd have to be out all night was all part of her game. He'd found her out just in time.

Cass didn't get to sleep for hours, and he didn't wake up until long after dawn. He refused the breakfast she had ready, and went to tinker around the engine for a minute or two. Then he went up to the cockpit and started the motor. The missing and backfiring was gone; it ran perfectly. He sulked as he ran the range markers up the Caloosahatchee, and ignored the pleading in Cupcake's eyes. The romance was gone—finished. The sooner he got rid of the girl the better.

It was near noon when the *Bon Temps* nosed into the Yacht Basin. Cass made a line fast, and without a word went to the dockmaster's office. He stayed there until he saw the girl go ashore with her grip. He went next to a sportsman's supply shop on Bay Street to look at fishing tackle, but his heart wasn't in it. He was depressed—low in spirits—and he decided to push on up the coast, but first he had to restock the larder. He went to a super-market and gave a boy a dollar to haul the stuff back to the boat.

When Cass returned to the *Bon Temps* he found a young man waiting alongside the slip. He was a reporter from the *News-Press.*

"Give me the whole story, will you, mister," the chap demanded. "Your name — where you're from — how you happened to find her — was she really lost down in the islands?—give me the whole works."

"What story?" Cass snorted. "What are you talking about?"

The reporter gave Cass a peculiar look. "You mean you don't know about her?"

"All I know," said Cass irritably, "is that a nurse was on a case down near Shark River, and asked me to bring her to town. I did, and that's all there is to it."

The reporter pulled a folded paper from his pocket, opened it to the front page, and shoved it in front of Cass. There was a picture of Cupcake, and a two column heading in large type.

HEIRESS AND PHILANTHROPIST ON MERCY MISSION MAY BE LOST IN TEN THOUSAND ISLAND REGION.

Ruth Jordan, 24, heiress to the Jordan Mining millions, and director of the famous Bayboro Settlement Foundation of New York, has not been heard from since she left for the Ten Thousand Island region by chartered plane last Thursday. It is not known if . . .

So that's who Cupcake really was! She had told him her name when she came aboard, but it hadn't registered. His heart seemed to be down in the pit of his stomach. She wasn't just plain Ruth Jordan, she was the Ruth Jordan! How stupid can a fellow get? Poor girl hunting a meal ticket—that was a laugh? She could buy and sell him a hundred times over, and never even miss the money. His mind was going around like a pinwheel. He turned abruptly and started across Edwards Drive toward the business section.

"Hey!" the startled reporter yelled, running after him, "Give me a story, will you?"

Cass stopped dead in his tracks. He grabbed the newsman's arm. "Tell me where Miss Jordan is staying and I'll give you a real story — later."

"She's registered at the Bradley Arms," the reporter gasped. "But it's no use—she won't see anybody,"

The desk clerk was apprehensive as the wild-eyed young man charged into the hotel lobby. Either the chap had been drinking, or something had given him a good scare. He knew the type; you had to humor them.

"What's the number of Miss Jordan's room?" Cass demanded.

"It's 514," said the clerk, but Miss Jordan gave orders not to be disturbed."

In the end it was the clerk who gave in. The hotel didn't like brawls in the lobby, so he finally agreed to call Miss Jordan's room. When he turned away from the switch-board he was rubbing his bald head, and looking perplex-ed. "I don't understand, Mr. Summers, but the lady said to tell you to go eat a cupcake. Those were her very words."

Cass went out on First Street and leaned against a royal palm. He'd certainly messed things up with his unwarrant-ed suspicions. He couldn't blame Cupcake for being sore— not after the fool he'd acted. Then he grasped at a fleet-ing idea. If he could only see Cupcake—talk to her for a minute—he might be able to patch things up. It was worth more than a try.

Cass went around to a side door, entered the lobby, and sneaked into the elevator when the clerk wasn't look-ing. He found the right room and knocked on the door. There was no answer, so he beat on the door with both fists—savagely. This time he heard her voice. It sounded like she had the sniffles. "Open up, Cupcake, I want to see you!" he shouted. He waited a brief moment, and when the door didn't open he pounded again. Then he heard a voice behind him.

Cass looked around to see a white haired lady stand-ing in the door of the room across the hall. "Go away, young man," she said firmly, "or I'll call the office."

There was only one sensible thing to do, and Cass did it. He went down and waited in the street in front of the hotel. It wouldn't have helped if he'd been arrested as a

hotel prowler, and the story might have gone out over the press wires. No, the only thing to do was to wait.

Cass waited all of two hours before Ruth Jordan came out of the hotel. She was out on the sidewalk before he recognized her. She was in a tricky dress and gold strapped sandals, and her hair was done differently. Cass was alongside in three bounds and took her arm. She didn't seem too surprised; in fact she'd rather expected he'd be nearby. She allowed him to hurry her across the street in the face of a red light. Not a word was said until they were back aboard the *Bon Temps*.

"I'm a heel, Cupcake—or anything else you want to call me," Cass began when they were side by side in deck chairs. "All I'm asking is that you listen . . . After that, if you say so, I'll check out . . . "

While Ruth listened with her eyes on her hands, Cass poured out all the things that had troubled his mind. In cold type a lot of it would have appeared rather senseless, but the emotion in his voice made it all sound logical. When he finished there was silence for almost a half minute. Then her hand strayed, seeking his. It gave him just the extra spot of courage he needed.

"That's it, Cupcake," he begged. "Can't we start over?"
She leaned towards him. "As of now," she whispered.
After a time Cass looked up. There was a row of people lining the cement balustrade on Edwards Drive, and watching with considerable interest. He was too happy to care, so he kissed Ruth again so that the spectators would get their money's worth.

*   *   *   *

It was really quite a sendoff. The harbormaster had spread the word, and all the boats in the Basin let loose with hoots and whistles as the *Bon Temps* glided out into the river. As soon as they were out in the channel and heading for the Gulf, Cass grabbed his bride and held her close.

"Look, Cupcake," he spoke severely, "one thing's got to be settled right off. We're going to live on my income, see? What you do with yours is your affair."

"You're the skipper," she said meekly. Then he saw a mischievous gleam creep into her eyes. "There's one thing I have to tell you," she began guiltily. "Remember the other evening down by Sanibel—when the engine acted up? Well, it was because I turned the valve on the gasoline line—to keep us from getting to Fort Myers that night."

Cass didn't look surprised. "It was the first thing I discovered," he smiled, "I figured I knew why you did it, and I decided to go along with the gag."

"And I knew that you knew it," Ruth laughed happily. Then she gave his nose a tweak, and Cass gathered her in his arms. After a minute she broke loose and started for the cabin.

"What now?" he called after her.

She looked back from the hatchway and offered a saucy smile. "I'm going to bake you a big mess of cupcakes, skipper," she sang out. "They'll be in the bread-box—just in case you get hungry—tonight."

The Yellow Quitter

THE FOLLOWING TALE happened at a small highway filling station near Clearwater some thirty years ago. The story was told to me in all detail by a clerk who worked in a general store across the road from Red's garage-filling station, and as soon as I returned to my home in Fort Myers I typed it up and sent it to *Detective Magazine* in New York. It was purchased on its first time out, and appeared in the September 15th 1934, issue of the magazine. Because it was an unusual case it is here reprinted for the first time. The store clerk was the only witness to the actual holdup, and he relates the happenings in his own words.

— : —

"I wouldn't have been loafing around Red's filling station near midnight except it was a Saturday, and I was on my way home from a date with the future wife. You know how it is when you've spent a whole evening on a porch swing with the girl you hope to marry? Your blood's hot and tingling, and you use 'most any excuse to keep from calling it a day. You just don't want to hit the hay and turn out the light. Besides, Red's wife was in a bad way and I wanted to ask about her.

"When I came by Red's place he was counting the money, and about ready to close up. It was a dangerous

thing to do so late at night because there'd been holdups around Clearwater and St. Pete, and I told him so. For an answer he took me around behind the counter and showed me the scheme he'd rigged up to greet anybody who tried to clean out his cash register."

"I'll blow the living hell out of anybody who tries to steal my money," he told me. "I'll do it for—for Ruth's sake."

"I understood what he meant. If you'd been there to have seen the light in his eyes you'd have known that he meant it, too. Ruth, of course, was Red's wife, and a mighty swell girl. They'd been married a little over a year, and up to the time of the wedding she'd been a healthy looking tomboy sort, the kind of girl everybody's crazy about. Then she started ailing—sudden like—a leaking valve in the heart, the doctors said. Of course Red was near nuts with worry, and he was almost flat broke from paying bills. The girl needed a serious type of operation—soon—and there was only one ray of hope left.

A heart specialist in Philadelphia had heard about the case, and he'd offered to do the job free if Red would take Ruth north. It wouldn't cost anything but the train fare, meals and a cheap room for Red while Ruth was in the hospital—but Red didn't have enough. He was trying to save it up, and he'd been trying to sell the business, but no buyer had shown up. All the cash he had in the world was in the cash drawer.

"Just then I heard a car jar to a stop outside, followed by quick steps on the cement. Red dumped the money back in the register, and turned around, ready to see what the late customer wanted. A man in a rumpled suit and a beat-up hat down low on his eyes came in the door. I looked around and saw he had us covered with a gun."

"Stick 'em up — high!" the man ordered. The voice wasn't loud, but it penetrated. Like you'd been stabbed with a knife. A cold spot—imagination, of course—felt like it was freezing my guts. I think a lump leaped into my

throat. Don't get me wrong! I wasn't scared for myself—honest. It was the idea that flashed in my brain. I was about to see a man die!

"I pulled my eyes away from the bandit long enough to glance at Red. He had backed to the wall, and his arms were up over his head—high. I'll never forget the look on his face. It was white and twisted—sort of hellish looking. He was staring down at the stranger's feet. I figured he was getting ready to jerk on the wire; ready to spring the trap. Birdlike I tried to keep my eye on Red and the hold-up man at the same time. One was cold, calm deadly; the other was damp with sweat and trembling."

"Keep 'em up, buddies!" the bandit snarled. "Try anything and you'll get a slug—both of you!"

"The guy went around the end of the counter and stopped by the register. I was glad I wasn't in his shoes. A few minutes before Red had shown me the outfit he'd fixed up in case he was held up. Now I was going to see it work. I wished I was miles away instead of having to see what was going to happen to the guy in the crummy suit.

"The bandit kept us covered as he reached to open the cash drawer. Knowing what I did I wanted to yell a warning. It's hard to see a man about to die—even if he's a thieving, yellow rat. But what could I do? I remembered about Ruth, and tried to swallow my swollen tongue. My God, but it was awful.

"Now the guy had his hand on the NO SALE key. I heard the bell ring as the drawer flew open. I had seen the shotgun nailed in place under the counter, aimed for anyone standing in front of the register. I had seen the wire attached to the trigger, and running around the walls through staples, and as high as a man could reach. One jerk on the wire would do the trick.

"Now was the time! I looked at Red. The sweat was running down his face. His fingers were cupped around the taunt wire. He was shaking all over like he had chills and fever. Why didn't he pull on the wire? Why didn't he get it over with? Why didn't he...............?

"Suddenly I got the idea that Red was stalling. It flashed over me that he didn't have the guts to go through with it. I heard the air rush out of my mouth. I'd been holding my breath for a full minute. I had a funny feeling deep inside. All of a sudden I was glad I wasn't having to look down on a bloody, quivering mess on the floor. At the same time I was mad because Red was a yellow quitter. I was all mixed up.

"Then I tried to reach the wire myself. I don't honestly know if I would have pulled it even if I'd been able to reach it. For once in my life—after it was all over—I was glad I was a shorty, only a little over five feet tall. Red was six feet two or better. That's the way life is; first you want something, then you don't.

"The bandit cleaned out the till and jammed the money—what little there was—into his coat pocket. He ran to the door, keeping us both covered."

"Lousy cheap skates," he sneered. "less than ten bucks. I ought to blast you for wasting a man's time. Hold everything!"

"The guy slammed the door shut, and we heard the tires squeal as he drove off. There was no use going after him. The only gun in the place was nailed tight under the counter. When I looked around I saw Red down on the floor. I thought he had fainted. Then he got up and fell into a chair. He was dazed looking; like something had hit him over the head. I stood and looked at him in disgust, the coward! I wondered why he had a fist drawn up in a tight knot. The skin over his knuckles was white. I wondered about a lot of things. Then I spoke.

"So you're the brave guy—the guy who was all set for a holdup. Hell! You were so scared your tail was drooping. I thought you had nerve. I thought you had guts. I thought Ruth.................."

"Red motioned for me to stop. He mopped his face with his dirty sleeve, and got up. There was a goofy look on his face—he was still trembling. His voice was choked up.

"I couldn't—couldn't kill the guy," he gasped. "Not after he gave me—and Ruth—the first decent break we've had."

"I guess I looked at him like he'd gone complete nuts. Anyway he gulped a couple times and shook himself like a wet dog. Then he stood up straight and faced me.

"I know you think I turned yellow. Well I didn't. You didn't see this ...."

"He opened his fist and showed me what he'd been holding. He'd been holding it so tight there were four white finger dents in his palm.

"It fell out of his picket when he jerked out the gun. I saw it fall—there close to the door. All the time I was praying that he wouldn't miss it—see it. All I wanted was to get him gone—quick. Tell people goodbye for me, will you? I'm taking Ruth to Philadelphia on the morning train."

As he wobbled out of the station I saw him fold the bit of green paper into a little square, and shove it into his watch pocket. I didn't blame him for being careful. A guy doesn't pick up many hundred dollar bills off the floor these days."

"...Not For All the Gold in Cuba"

ARRIVED IN MIAMI on the noon bus, put a job wanted ad in the *Herald* and had callers before noon the next morning. Two men called at my hotel room, and the big one did all the talking. His name was Al Randall, and he said he was the captain of a yacht, and in need of an engineer. The oily little fellow with him was a Cuban named Carlos Serpio, and his beady little eyes reminded me of snakes I'd seen in zoos.

The reason I was in Miami was to get away from the ice and snow of Lake Michigan, and get steady work the year round. I am a marine mechanic and engineer, and you can't work when everything's frozen in. Miami, with all the boats and yachts, looked like it was made to order.

Captain Randall said he was from Chicago and ready to set out on a treasure hunting expedition. He wanted an engineer for a week or two, and indicated there might be a bonus if the party had any luck. I didn't like the big man's looks any more than the Cuban's, and when he saw I was about to refuse he opened a wallet and tossed two one hundred dollar bills on the bed.

"That's for a starter," he said. "There'll be more like it when we get back."

The sight of the big bills changed my mind, and against

95

better judgement I took the job. The Captain scribbled an address on the back of a card.

"We'll meet there at eleven tonight," he ordered as I picked up the money. "Keep all this under your hat, understand! When you're after gold you don't want a lot of busybodies on your tail."

When night came I took my grip and tool kit and called a taxi. The address on the card turned out to be on Miami Beach near Hotel Row. It was a fancy cocktail lounge, and I ordered a beer and settled down in a booth to wait. During my second beer a girl—maybe about twenty-five and not an extra good looker—came to sit with me. She was talkative, but not drunk, and I bought her a drink just to be sociable and help pass the time. Her name was Inez and she was feeling sorry for herself. She'd been a dice girl at Las Vegas, but she'd been blacklisted due to a frameup, and now the best she'd been able to do in Miami was to get a job as cook aboard a yacht. Just then Captain Randall entered the bar, and I saw Inez hurry to meet him. It dawned on me, suddenly that we were to be shipmates.

At the parking lot we got into a station wagon loaded with boxes of groceries, cases of beer, five gallon jugs of water, and a long and heavy wooden box. I didn't know it at the time, but the box contained rifles and tommy-guns. Two strangers were crowded in the front seat beside Randall when we turned into Collins Avenue and headed north. One turned out to be a shifty eyed fellow named Slug Rother, and the other was a cauliflower eared ex-fighter they called Gyp Kelly. Something told me that it was a job that I should have passed up, but it was too late to back out.

In about ten minutes we passed through iron gates, drove beyond a boarded up mansion, and stopped beside a large boathouse. By midnight we had all the stuff loaded aboard the sleek fifty footer, and I had the engines warmed up. In a few minutes we were out of Indian Creek, and

Captain Randall headed for Government Cut and the open sea. The twin Diesels purred beautifully, and after a time I fell asleep on a bunk beside the port motor.

It was near dawn when I woke up and climbed up the ladder to look around. I could see Captain Randall's face dimly lit from the binnacle light, and then I noticed something else. A freshly painted amateurish sign reading, MARLINE hung from wires over the original name of the yacht, which proved to be the WINDMERE. For the first time it dawned on me that the yacht was stolen. Perhaps we were going south to join Fidel Castro's navy. In any case I was in a spot; all I could do was to keep my eyes open.

We kept south until the Cuban coast became a hazy mist, then zigzagged back and forth until night was upon us. Then, when we were about a mile from shore, and with all lights out, we came to anchor. Then the Cuban, Rother and Kelly lowered the launch and headed towards some faint lights on shore. After a time I went on deck and stood by the rail. I could see nothing in the moonless, cloud covered sky, but suddenly I felt a hand on my arm. Inez became to whisper close to my ear.

"I'm afraid there'll be trouble," she hissed. I heard them talking—that nasty Cuban guy used to manage a gambling casino for Chicago gangsters — when the revolution came he buried a lot of money somewhere; now they've gone to dig it up."

Inez told me more, but that was the main idea. She was really scared, and to tell the truth, I was, too. I'd never have taken the job if I'd seen Rother and Kelly in the first place. They looked like the hoods you see in crime movies.

A couple of hours passed. Then came the sound of shooting ashore. It stopped almost as soon as it began, and a few minutes later I heard the exhaust of the launch coming towards us. Rother and Kelly were the only ones in the boat when they came alongside, and I heard them grunt and curse as they hoisted something heavy on deck. Then, with the anchor up, Randall called for full speed and we headed west.

After what seemed like an hour the girl, Inez, came into the engine room. By the instrument panel light I could see that she was white with fright. She grabbed my arm with both hands and pulled close. I could feel her trembling.

"They're going to kill us," she managed to choke out. "I heard them talking through a ventilator—they plan to double cross the Chicago gang, hide out in Mexico, sink the yacht and kill you and me. Oh, why did I ever come to Miami..............?"

We talked more, and I'll have to give the girl credit—she had guts under the bleached, blond head of hers. I looked around and knew what I was going to have to do. The engine room was lined with steel plates, and the fire doors in the bulkheads had metal bolts. In case of gun fire it could be made the safest place on the yacht.

"Go out and get a gun if you can," I told Inez. "Bring some food and water, too, but don't let them see you."

The girl was back in a minute. She brought a gallon jug of mineral water, a loaf of bread, and an automatic she picked up in Rother's cabin. I made sure there was a full clip in the weapon, then bolted the bulkhead doors and jammed the hatch in the closed position. For the time being we were safe, and if the men came after us I could easily wreck both engines with a wrench. Without the engines the yacht would be sitting duck wallowing there in the Gulf Stream.

Nothing happened until daylight, and then Randall began calling for Inez. A couple of minutes later one of the men—it was Kelly—pounded on the bulkhead door. When I didn't open they tried to shot away the bolt, but it didn't work. Then Captain Randall called down from above, but when I didn't answer he cursed the girl and me, and began to make threats. After that there was quiet for a spell. I imagined they were holding a council of war, and trying to decide what to do next. I kept the engines going. There wasn't any sense in shutting them down when we were so far from any shore.

Randall and his two hoods must have been thinking the same thing. In any case they didn't bother us any more, and I guess they were glad I hadn't put the engines out of commission. They were sure they could do away with us when the right time came. I was getting around to the same opinion, but I wasn't ready to give up.

About an hour after daylight I looked out of a porthole and saw a boat some three or four miles distant, and it was on a parallel course. Then, like the blast of a missile, an idea shot into my mind. I wanted to keep on living, and it might be my only chance. I jerked open my tool kit and grabbed a pair of visegrip pliers. You know; the kind that you can clamp on a round object and they'll hold on as tight as grim death to a dead cat.

I leaped on top of the narrow engine room work bench and reached up to the rudder cable. The wire rope came down from the pilot house through a tube, then passed over an open sheave, and back to the rudder in the stern. I clamped one of the visegrips on each side of the steel pulley, so the cable couldn't move and the yacht couldn't be steered by the men above.

Before Randall or the other two realized what was happening, I had idled the port engine and raced the starboard motor. The bow of the yacht began to swing to port and head in the direction of the distant craft. Howls came from the men above, but there was nothing they could do for the moment.

For once luck came to stand by me. When the other boat saw our sudden change of direction, she altered her course and came towards us at full speed. When the stranger was about a mile distant I recognized her as being a Coast Guard cutter, and I knew Inez and I were saved.

When the cutter was close by I cut the yacht's engines, then waited while the Coast Guarder lowered a boat and and sent an officer and four men to check on the yacht's strange behavior.

There is little more to tell. Randall, Rother and Kelly were held at Key West and charged with yacht stealing and several other crimes. There was no indictment for Serpio's murder because the killing was done in Castro's Cuba, and there wasn't a body for evidence. Inez and I were held as material witnesses for a time, and then released. The money the men had brought from Cuba—over three hundred and fifty thousand, most of it in gold—was impounded by the Government.

As soon as we were set free, Inez and I went to a bar on Simonton Street. We had a couple of beers to celebrate the fact that we were where we were, and not crab food on the bottom of the Gulf off the Mexican coast. All of a sudden the girl leaned over, grabbed my head between her hands, and planted a kiss in the right place. When she tried to repeat I was ready and pushed her away. Then, for the first time, I showed her some pictures in my wallet. They were of my pretty little wife and two kids—a girl and a boy—back in Michigan. Inez looked them over and began to cry.

"Gee!" she said as she dabbed at her eyes, "Some girls have all the luck, but never me."

A little later I saw Inez board a bus for Miami. The District Attorney had asked me to stick around for a few days in case I was needed, and while I was waiting I landed a good job in Key West, and sent for the wife and kids to join me. After that I had one other lucky break. The wealthy man who owned the WINDMERE sent me a check for a thousand dollars for keeping the yacht from being sunk or burned by the gangsters.

In spite of the way things have turned out you can bet I wouldn't want to go through the whole deal over again. No, not for all the gold in Castro's Cuba!

The Early History of Fort Myers

Author's Note: Captain Francis Asbury Hendry served both the Union and the Confederate forces at different times in his eventful life. In this rambling account of his activities, which he dictated about 1908, he gives a comprehensive picture of what all of South Florida was like in the 1850s, and during the Civil War. He was born in Georgia in 1833, and died in 1917.

HE FIRST historical account we have of Fort Myers is when it was occupied by the Unites States Military on November 4th, 1841. It was abandoned March 21st, 1842, being occupied but a few months. The place was named then in honor of Lieutenant John H. Harvie, who had died, probably from campaign exposure, about two months before the place was established. From 1842 to 1850 there is nothing known of the place, and it appears that it was almost forgotten.

It was February 14th, 1850, when General Twiggs ordered Major Ridgely to take command of two companies of regular soldiers and proceed to the mouth of the Caloosahatchee, ascend that river and select the most eligible point on its southern bank and establish a military post, clear away the forest, fortify, unfurl Old Glory to the breeze, and to name the place Fort Myers, in honor of Colonel Abraham C. Myers, a distinguished veteran of the Mexican War, and at that time the chief Quartermaster of the war department of Florida. This officer, when the war between the States in 1861 became inevitable, like the beloved Robert E. Lee, resigned his commission and cast his lot with the destiny of South Carolina, his native state, and was lost sight of.

While we have lost sight of Col. Myers, the City of Fort Myers is, today, a living monument to his memory, more to be appreciated than marble or stone. The place selected by Major Ridgely was the old site of Fort Harvey, and he gave it the new name of Fort Myers. For the next eight eventful years the post was occupied by the army, and was the scene of great activity during the time of Indian warfare and Indian migration to the far West. It was to Fort Myers that the United States Indian Agent, Colonel Rector brought his delegation of friendly Indians from Arkansas, and finally induced the fearless and indomitable Billy Bowlegs to yield to the sceptre of Uncle Sam, and turn on his native home, the wilds of Florida, and with most of his tribe migrate to the far West, never to return. That big chief was not scared into the terms offered by Uncle Sam, but he could, savage as he was, read the handwriting upon the wall and interpret it correctly. The days of his glory had departed, and he gracefully accepted the fact.

It was about June 1st, 1858, when Fort Myers was abandoned by the United States forces. In 1859 the fort was occupied by a civil force, under the management of Major James Evans. It was an incorporated company from Virginia, whose object was to engage in the culture of fruits and all kinds of tropical plants common to the tropics and this latitude. Many slaves were brought down from Virginia for the purpose of clearing the land, and fitting it for that promising industry. The great war between the states caused the abandonment of this project, and the place was again uninhabited, and exposed to fire and general devastation.

Four years later, while the destiny of our country was trembling in the scales of uncertainty, the Federal soldiers took possession of Fort Myers and made it headquarters for all manner of mischief common to warfare. Frequent and destructive raids were made far into the interior and into Confederate lines, causing much distress to the devotee of the Southern cause. Large herds of cattle were rounded up by Federal cavalry and driven down to Fort Myers and there slaughtered for use of the garrison, and the blockading squadron of Sanibel Island in San Carlos Bay. A large number were carried on transports to Pine Island, landing about where St. James is now situated. So annoying was the condition that an unsuccessful attempt was made by Colonel J. C. Munnerlyn's battalion, commanded by Major William Footman, to capture and destroy the place, resulting, however, in its evacuation. Major Footman, after formally demanding a surrender and being denied, raised a terrible racket. A day was spent in cannon and rifle practice, and a battle of sorts followed. One man was killed, a lot of pickets, horses and cattle were captured, was the result so far as Major Footman knew, but the most desired result was going on inside the fort. While Major Footman was retracing his steps, having given up the undertaking as a bad job, the Federals were packing up and hurrying down the river to Punta Rassa and placing themselves under cover of their gunboats. The failure to capture the place at that time, under the circumstances connected with it, was as might have been expected.

Two hundred and seventy-five men poorly armed with one field piece attacking five companies of well armed men with block houses, breastworks and three field pieces mounted at commanding points, could not expect success. While the Confederates did not hurt the enemy very much, they gave him a terrible fright for the next morning the nest was warm but the bird had flown.

In mentioning this little unpleasantness in which Fort Myers played a conspicuous part, mention should be made of the fact that Major Footman completely surprised the garrison when he sent in his flag of truce and politely demanded an unconditional surrender, except that the officers and men be treated as prisoners of war. A picket post was a mile out from the front, with ten men armed with Enfield rifles. This fact Major Footman ascertained from a reliable source, and he was determined to capture that picket guard.

The night preceding the attack on Fort Myers the battalion was marching leisurely along the trail between Fort
Thompson and Fort Myers, and came to a halt about twelve
miles from Fort Myers. It was dark and raining, and Major
Footman called for me. He said: "Captain, I want ten men
who can step on eggs and not break them. Make a detail
from your company, dismount them and place them in command of one of your best lieutenants, and have him report
to me at once." This order was quickly complied with,
when Lieutenant George W. Hendry, in command of ten
men of his own choosing, reported to Major Footman.

The Major said to him in substance, that there was a
picket post one mile from Fort Myers on a little creek
(Billy's Creek), and to capture the pickets without firing
a gun if possible. The Lieutenant had a hard, difficult and
perilous job before him, and he came as near to accomplish-
ment as was possible for him to do. The country was so covered with water, the night so dark, and the pickets without
campfires, that it was impossible to locate them. He passed
within yards of the guard and did not know it. The picket
guard heard the wading in the water, but thought it was a
herd of cattle passing by. When the day dawned Lientenant
Hendry returned to the battalion, meeting it a few miles
from Fort Myers.

The Major was still determined to capture the picket
post, and ordered Lieutenant William M. Hendry, of Captain Wall's company, to select from the whole battalion ten
men and make a dash upon the picket post. This Lieutenant
Hendry was no other than our present "Uncle Marion"
Hendry, the present clerk of the Lee County Circuit Court.
The order was to capture without firing a gun, if possible.
This was a dangerous procedure. It meant ten men attacking ten well armed men in a carefully selected position.
The instructions were simple and to the point; when within
one half mile of the picket post they were to dash at full
speed, and to maintain that speed until they dashed into the
picket camp. Well does the writer remember seeing the
water fly from under the heels of the chargers in that mad

dash, and the spirit and determined look of those cavalry-
men. The writer can't recall all the names of the men com-
posing that charge, but some were Lt. William M. Hendry,
now of Fort Myers; Frank Saxon of Brooksville, Gideon
Zipperer of Bartow, and Benjamin F. Blount of Bartow.
I am sorry not to be able to recall the names of the others.
No more daring charge was made during the great war.
There was not a gun fired and every picket was trotting
back to our rear in a few minutes, and became our prisoners
of war.

Many interesting incidents occurred in that march and
campaign against Fort Myers which spaces forbids mention.
Soon after, the mad dash for the fort was hastily abandoned; this time in confusion and haste, leaving three substan-
tial block houses, three dismounted batteries, and a long
crescent-shaped breastworks extending from the site of the
Royal Palm Hotel, around to the river at the foot of Hendry
Street, all of which has been leveled, leaving no signs today.
The old fort, blessed with so many natural advantages and
attractions, and so beautifully situated on the broad Caloosahatchee, was destined to be reoccupied at no distant day.

Three years later real settlers began to occupy Fort
Myers, and it was never to be abandoned again. In 1858 the
International Ocean Telegraph Company obtained a twen-
ty-year charter to operate a telegraph line through the
state, and to run a submarine cable to Key West and Cuba.
This line was completed the following year, and the wires
passed by Fort Myers enroute to Punta Rassa, which point
was the landing of the cable, which gave inspiration to those
who desired to make Fort Myers their home.

About this time a cattle-shipping point was established
at Punta Rassa, and Fort Myers became the headquarters
for large cattle dealers from Cuba. The demand in Cuba
for Florida cattle became very extensive, and Spanish
ounces of gold, as well as doubloons, became almost play-
things. Cattle were driven from all over the state, and even
from Georgia, and shipped to these beef-eating people.

These conditions attracted many who fell in love with Fort Myers and made it their home. Fort Myers had its share of vicissitudes, of rough and toughs, common to all frontier countries, but its tendency was always to become a good place to live.

It is not my purpose to tell of the Fort Myers of today. I will confine this writing to telling of the times when it was clothed in its military garb, in full uniform and on dress parade. I first saw Fort Myers in 1853 when its personnel was composed of such men as General Hancock, who afterwards ran on the Democratic ticket for President of the United States; Colonel Harvie Brown, the commandant; Lieutenant Hartsuff; Lieutenant Benson, Captain Fowler, for whom Fowler Street was named, and others. Lieutenant Benson later bacame a general in the army and was killed at Malvern Hill, Virginia, in the Civil War.

There are few living today who can tell much of old Fort Myers from personal knowledge, and none who ever visited when it was known as Fort Harvie. However I was one who was wined and dined in Fort Myers in 1853—fifty-seven years ago—as a welcome guest among these noble men. Still the memory is fresh and vivid. Tampa was the headquarters for the military of the Florida Department, and all communications came from there.

The writer well remembers the steamer *Grey Cloud*, commanded by Captain Dukes of Tampa. She was to my mind a beautiful boat. I first saw her in Tampa as she steamed up that little, shallow, tortuous channel and tied up to an insignificant little dock, direct from Fort Myers, in the year 1851, two years before I visited Fort Myers for the first time. I believe she was the first steamboat I ever saw, being at that time about seventeen years old.

The next time I saw that beautiful boat she was just below Fort Denaud, at a post called Fort Simmons, on the Caloosahatchee. I was a volunteer in Captain Leroy G. Lesley's mounted company in U. S. service, and was detailed to assist in discharging a cargo from the *Grey Cloud*. This was in 1857. Other boats doubtless did much service in those days, but the *Grey Cloud* is the only one I can recall.

My second visit to Fort Myers was in 1853 or '54. I came in the capacity of a guide for Lieutenant Benson and party from Fort Meade, a distance of about a hundred miles. All was a trackless, uninhabited wilderness. The object of the trip was to ascertain if it was practical to open a road between the two posts. The party consisted of Lieutenant Benson, mounted, three pack mules, six footmen, and myself on horseback as guide. For this service I received one dollar per day in gold.

To tell of the events of that trip would be interesting, but space forbids. Fort Myers in that day was a veritable oasis in the desert. Uncle Sam never did things by halves, and Fort Myers was as neat and clean as a new pin. The city, today, may feel proud of herself, but it would be hard to excell the way the place looked when dressed in her military finery of those far years.

Fruit trees did not then exist, but forest trees of shade and beauty were most carefully selected, dressed and trimmed to suit the most fastidious taste for natural scenery. The paved streets and sidewalks were not there, but the walkways were made of carefully selected shells—not the common oyster shells, but shell from the Gulf beaches. There were beautifully green lawns, all kept immaculately clean. The long line of uniformed soldiers with white gloves and muskets as bright as new coins, and the officers with their golden epaulets and burnished side arms, were a sight to see.

The quarters of the post were the personification of neatness and cleanliness. Special care was given to the rock-rimmed river banks, and every tree, oak and palm were scrupulously preserved. The large commissary and sutler's store were filled and tastily arranged. The wagon yard and stables were exceptionally well kept, and the horses, mules and milk cows were as fat and sleek as corn, oats and hay could make them. All were groomed to perfection. The garrison garden was cared for by expert gardeners, and supplied the wants of the garrison with as fine vegetables as man ever ate.

My pen should not fail to describe the hospital, with its well filled drug store. This was said to have cost thirty thousand dollars. It stood about where the Royal Palm Hotel was to be erected many years later. Here Lieutenant Hartsuff, poor fellow, was to slowly recover from his wounds after being shot by Billy Bowlegs on Christmas morning of 1855. It happened while he was on duty some sixty miles southeast of Fort Myers. Billy Bowlegs stole a dapple grey horse from the picket line, then charged around the massacre camp, shooting at everyone. Lieutenant Hartsuff, badly wounded, hid in the saw grass, and thus escaped death.

Captain Thomas F. Quinn wrote me from Fort Spokane, Washington Territory, under date of March 19th, 1889, that he was one of the rescuing party and found Hartsuff nearly dead from wounds and exposure, within a few hundred yards of the block house at Fort Simon Drum. He was a drummer boy then, only fourteen years old. When he wrote me he was a captain of an infantry company. He says Hartsuff's command was made up at Fort Myers, and marched for their final campaign on December 14th, 1855. Their Christmas Day was ushered in by the yells and war whoops of the red devils near Billy's town. This was the beginning of hostilities of the Indian War of 1855-'57, and ending in 1858, as above. During the eventful period old Billy played havoc with the frontier settlements. He killed John Carney between his plow handles on the banks of the Alafia River. He killed Lieutenant Alderman Carlton, a very dear uncle of mine, and William Parker and Scott Whidden near Fort Meade. Two days later he killed George Powell and Robert Prince. He killed Starnes and Hinson near Tampa, and Captain John Parker at Royal Palm Hammock.

Many others were killed by his unerring rifle fire during this period. Old Billy was raised and brought up in a way that fitted him for this bloody work. Old Tiger Tail and Sam Jones, big chiefs and his predecessors, were past masters in the art of such work. Old Zack Taylor, of Mexican War fame, says that the hottest fight of his life was against those old warriors on Taylor's Creek, near Okeechobee Lake. One hundred and thirteen men fell dead or wounded within two hours time. Colonel Thompson for whom Fort Thompson was named was killed there.

I can't for want of space, tell more of the bloody events of the old time Indian Wars. Uncle Sam had to pay more than twenty million dollars in his attempts to force the Seminole Indians to migrate to the Indian Territory in the far West. A remnant of the tribe were left in the wilds of Florida; they being too stubborn and patriotic to leave the land of flowers. This remnant today are Indians to the manor born, never surrendering to Uncle Sam, and they look upon Billy Bowlegs as a traitor to the cause of Indian rights and liberty.

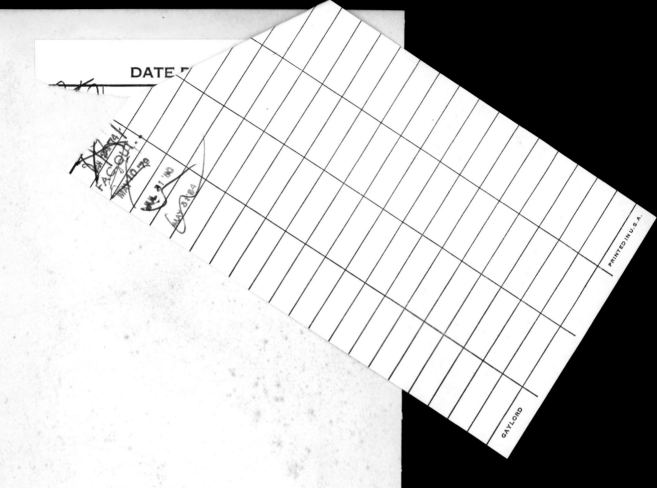